The Life and Times of

LIBERTY FALLS

PART TWO

Susan K. Jones

International Resourcing Services, Inc.
Northbrook, Illinois

CREDITS

Book Design and Graphics: Marvin Glick Design

All photos and illustrations provided by Corbis-Bettmann.

Table of Contents

Acknowledgments

My continuing inspiration for chronicling the history of Liberty Falls is the original creator of this fascinating Colorado town, Ralph P. Gadiel. Ralph's endless enthusiasm for the adventures of the Old West helps fuel my quest for the dramas and real-life details that bring Liberty Falls to life in print. My sincere thanks also to the very capable and very organized Deborah Gimza of International Resourcing Services for turning the manuscript into this handsome finished volume. I thank my husband, William T. Jones, and my two sons, W. Shannon Jones and Scott C. Jones, for their understanding when I spent many nights and weekends "in Liberty Falls" during the creation of this book. They could still see me sitting at the computer, but they knew that my thoughts had transported me to Old Colorado! Their support is very much appreciated. I thank my mother — Janet D. Kraus — for her excitement about Liberty Falls buildings and pewter figurines: and especially those of you who purchased Volume I of this book. Your love of Liberty Falls — and your intense interest in every facet of life there — made this second book possible!

CHAPTER I

All the Comforts of a Colorado Home

A glimpse into turn-of-the-century homelife in Liberty Falls...as told by a long-time resident and proud shopkeeper and homemaker, Mrs. Tully

Land sakes! It seems like just yesterday that Mr. Tully and I opened our first General Store here in Liberty Falls, but it's been nigh on to 40 years now! Built that little log cabin shop with our own hands, the Mister and I did — and as fast as we could, soon as we got to Colorado. You see, the miners needed most everything you can imagine, and in those days we were out in the wilds hereabouts! Hungry, cold, tired miners'd pay just about any price for a home-cooked meal or a warm blanket or such-like.

A happy group of Liberty Falls lads practice their skills at "leap frog" during Middle School recess.

Yes, in the old days the Mister and I had just about the only retail establishment in these parts. We carried food, clothes, tools, building supplies — even animal feed until Swanson's Feed and Grain opened up! At first we couldn't offer a very fancy line or much variety, but once the Union Pacific

Liberty Falls youngsters are always inventive when it comes to thinking up games and amusements. The boy below has challenged his friend to stay balanced while he walks all the way down this narrow wooden fence!

1

Railroad line opened up through Liberty Falls, we could order most anything from Back East — or even fashions from Europe or tea from China — and be pretty sure it'd get here in one piece.

Those were the days — back in the 1860s and '70s afore all these specialty retailers came into town and drew off most of our trade! Why, the Mister and I had money flowing in beyond our wildest dreams! We knew right quick that we'd made the best decision to come here. You see, when we heard about the Gold Rush in Colorado, the Mister thought on it for a spell and decided that mining would be too risky. But he felt sure that at least some of the miners would strike it rich. "And then they'll need food...warm clothes...more tools...and on and on!" he told me. "If we head out to Colorado now, we can find a place where the miners congregate and set up our own little General Store!"

My husband was right, I'm proud to tell you. Business was brisk from the day we arrived. Why, miners started buying provisions and tools right off our wagon before we even set up shop! They'd bid up the price on the simplest things, since just about every type of item they needed was scarce as hen's teeth! Maybe you've even heard the story I tell about the miner who paid me six dollars for a simple home-cooked breakfast...and peeled off the bills from a bankroll that would choke a horse! Mining's still a pretty well-paid profession. Mrs. Applegate at the boarding house tells me that even now "her boys" bring home about $3.50 per day.

Well, back to my story. Eventually, we built ourselves this storefront where we still do business today — and at first, the Mister and the youngsters and I all lived upstairs. We saved and saved until we had enough money stashed away to build us our very own "dream house" up on the hill. Maybe you've seen it? It's made of native Colorado stone and it has a peaked roof, bay windows, and my favorite part of all — the sun porch. Nothing as fancy as what the bankers and mining magnates have, but to the Mister and me, "Tully House" is heaven on earth!

And we earned that house with the sweat of our brows, I promise you! Why, even the youngsters helped out. They'd sweep the floor in the store, re-stock the shelves, pick up and deliver the mail at the train station, take orders to folks who were homebound, and even wait on customers in the afternoon. At home, the youngsters took turns gathering wood chips and drying them in the oven so they could be used to light the fire the next morning. They'd help me with the dishwashing, cleaning and other chores, too. They knew they had it easier than many of the children they went to school with: why, the farmers' daughters and sons often had to rise at 4:30 a.m. to feed the cattle and horses and clean the animals' stalls every day before breakfast!

In my day, children were taught that laziness was the worst sin of all! Each of my children learned to sew — even the boys can sew on their own buttons and stitch up rips and tears. The girls learned fancy needlework stitches and created samplers to show them off — I have them hanging proudly all over my house! In fact, one of my girls made a cross-stitch sampler that carried this wonderful old poem about working hard and liking it, surrounded by rosettes and all the letters of the alphabet:

Love Your Work!

Silly people don't like to work,
Let us try to love it;
Grave and great ones of the land
They are not above it.

Lazy people all get dull,
Mind and body weary;
Waking ones grow strong and bright
Time is never dreary.

Elder sisters, you may work,
Work and help your mothers,
Darn the stockings, mend the shirts,
Father's things and brothers.

Younger sisters, you may help,
Help by minding baby.
Little hands and little feet
Very useful may be.

Mrs. Tully taught all of her youngsters how to sew and mend. Here, a Liberty Falls lass practices her skill at threading a needle.

It wasn't "all work and no play" for my youngsters, though — we always found time for games and enjoyable pastimes, too. Each child had a small plot of land in the back yard where they could grow vegetables or flowers as they preferred. And we'd always take the finest specimens to the County Fair to compete for prizes. We had all manner of pets over the years: mostly dogs and bunnies. The children loved ice skating, swimming and parlor games, too — everything from "Blindman's Buff" to "Let's Pretend." But that seems long ago now. I'm teaching these games to my grandchildren these days, and Liberty Falls is so big and bustling that Main Street's starting to look like the Big City!

Why, nowadays we have just about every kind of store or service you can imagine right here on Main Street. There's Berghoff the butcher, Howard the hardware man, and even special stores for ladies' hats and for quilts! A big retail chain called May Company is buying up local stores in some of the towns in these parts, too — they've already claimed locations in Leadville and Cripple Creek. I wouldn't be surprised if there's a May Company store in Liberty Falls soon.

Our General Store has actually turned into a sort of a specialty shop and social center. For instance, take a look at those fancy tea canisters over there. We bring in a dozen or more different kinds of imported tea that our lady customers seem to specially like. We stock about a hundred varieties of penny candy, each in its own glass jar, so we see quite a bit of the little ones in town. And there's always a couple or more old coots sitting in here near the wood stove in the winter time playing checkers or whittlin', and some of my older customers still seem to prefer getting their yard goods here — calicos and muslins and such.

The Mister and I are gettin' up there in years now anyways, and our youngsters are grown with families of their own. So we've cut back our hours some and we take time to enjoy our friends and homelife more than ever before. And let me tell you — the modern way of homemaking sure is a far piece easier on a woman than it was in the old days! Anyone who wants it and can afford it today can have running water, sanitary sewers, electric light, and even a telephone, right in the home!

The Mister joined The Knights of Labor, Liberty Falls chapter, and took the job of Secretary. One of his duties is to create the fancy gold-sealed document that a widow gets when her lodge-member husband goes to his reward. Here's how they read:

"Whereas (Lodge Member's Name) has been called before the Great Master Workman of the Universe, we his faithful lodge brothers do express our earnest sympathy and lasting admiration for his service to The Knights of Labor. He was a man of sterling qualities...etc. etc." — you get the idea.

The lodge brothers also use just about any excuse to hold a convention or a parade, too. But frankly, from what I can see, most of their activities revolve around playing billiards and swapping stories. After all the hard work that the Mister put in over the years to build a good life for me and the family, I don't begrudge him his time down at the lodge. In fact, I take some time off myself nowadays. Why, just last week I arranged a private railroad excursion for some of my friends and me to go out into the mountains to pick wildflowers. Everyone came back with bouquets and baskets full of flowers. It was glorious!

Another time we took the train to the Garden of the Gods in Colorado Springs. There you can see an amazing garden full of red sandstone rock formations that look for all the world like some kind of religious set-up. But it's completely natural — we hear-tell that the Pueblo Indians found it that way. The park is 1,350 acres in all, and the rocks are thought to be over 300 million years old. Formed by erosion, they were. There's a Trading Post down that way too, where you can buy Indian artifacts or even food for a picnic.

By the by, some of the Liberty Falls ladies are getting downright fashion-conscious. Why, we'll often get together for tea and pass around a copy of the latest "Harper's Bazaar" — that's the magazine that bills itself as "A Repository of Fashion, Pleasure and Instruction." We also compare notes on the latest contraptions we can use to make life more elegant hereabouts. There's the Pleating Iron (also known as the Fluting Iron) that can put pleats into a skirt as quick as you can say "by your leave." Then there's the lamp-heated Curling Iron that lets ladyfolks create a headful of curls for special occasions or Sunday-go-to-meeting. Most recently, I heard about a new product called the Gem Ice Shaver. I imagine we'll be having shaved ice in our drinks next time I'm invited up to Mrs. DuBois' or Mrs. Clark's in the summertime! And did you hear about Mrs. Clark's new bedroom suite? I was down at the train station when it arrived from Boston. It's fancy-carved and made of solid black walnut!

Now that the Mister and I are in our "golden years," we look back on the early days of Liberty Falls with satisfaction and pride. We helped build this thriving community — fed and clothed the miners, even provided a grubstake for a few gents who ran out of money before they hit gold! We raised our children here, and they've all married and stayed in town. And through it all we put our family first. A good homelife is the key to true happiness — that's my motto! Come visit us at the store sometime: we'll have a game of checkers or a good round of gossip. And I'll give your little ones some penny candy — on the house! See you then!

MRS. TULLY'S FAVORITE FAMILY ACTIVITIES

Here are some of the wholesome pastimes my youngsters and I devised way back when here in Liberty Falls. I reckon you and your young folks might enjoy them, too!

Visiting Duffy's Mill

When the children and I had a little time of an afternoon, we'd often stroll over to Duffy's Mill. Old Mr. Duffy always had time for us! If he was done grinding grain for the day, he'd let the children climb up into his grist mill wheel — always with a stern warning not to go anywhere near it when it was in action. Then he'd have the youngsters step up onto his grain scale one by one, and exclaim at how big they were getting! On warm days, the children often would swim in the pond beside the mill — or fish for a spell. And they'd tell tales about how their friends saw a scary white ghost one night at the mill. Then Mr. Duffy and I would exchange grins — why, that was no ghost, it was only old Duffy himself, covered with flour!

Updating the Family Circular

Now when the Mister and I came West, we left a large family behind in Kansas City. One of my sisters eventually moved to Texas, and one of the Mister's brothers now resides all the way out in California. So like many folks we know, we keep up to date on each others' doings with a Family Circular. Here's how it works. On the first day of each month, I take out a piece of paper and write for a spell about what we Tullys have been up to in Liberty Falls. In the old days I'd let each of the youngsters draw a picture or write a few words, too. Then I mail that to a sister, brother or cousin. When they get my letter, they add some news of their own and then mail the whole shebang to another relative. Eventually, the whole journal makes it back to us, so in the course of a few months, we hear the news from kinfolk all over creation!

A Parlor Game: Bag and Stick

I like this game especially well for a Christmas party when you have young folks from all over the neighborhood gathered at your house. Fill a paper bag with candies (penny candies from our store, if you can!) and hang it from the ceiling on a string. Blindfold one player and spin him around and around until he's completely lost his bearings. Give him a stick and tell him he has, say, three chances to hit and break open the bag of sweets. If he doesn't succeed, let other players try one by one until the bag of sweets is broken. Then there will be a mad dash to recover all the candies!

Conversation Lozenges

When my daughters were old enough for courting, I told them about these special, heart-shaped candies with messages printed on them like "Be Mine" or "I Pine for You." If a boy gives a girl a conversation lozenge, she has a choice to make. If she accepts it, she's signaling that the romance is underway. If she throws it back at him, he knows she has no interest. Sometimes girls carry conversation lozenges of their own to give away. For instance, a boy might give a young lady one that says, "Can I See You Home?" and she might counter with a candy reading, "You Are the Boy of My Heart."

Party Jokes

Here are some "funnies" to tell at your next get-together:

> *What do you call a hearty gentleman? Sir-loin!*
> *What do you call a positive gentleman? Cer-tain!*
> *What do you call a suspicious gentleman? Sur-mise!*
> *What do you call a cowardly gentleman? Sur-render!*

Smith and Jones were discussing the question of who was to be the head of the house, the man or the woman.

"I am the head of my establishment," said Jones. "I am the bread-winner. Why shouldn't I be?"

"Well," replied Smith, "before my wife and I were married, we made an agreement that I should make the rulings in all major things, my wife in all the minor."

"How has it worked?" queried Jones.

Smith smiled. "So far," he replied, "no major matters have come up!"

Jim: My teacher was angry with me today.
Father: Why was that?
Jim: I told her I didn't know where the Great Lakes were.
Father: Next time, remember where you put things!

CHAPTER II

Ladies in Business: The "Elegant Entrepreneurs"

The inspiring saga of three Liberty Falls ladies, making it on their own as successful merchants...as told by the proud owner of Aunt Alice's Quilt Shop, Alice Willoughby

You know, back in the pioneer days here in Liberty Falls, my women friends and I loved nothing more than to hold an old-fashioned quilting bee every so often. We'd gather our colorful fabric scraps, needles and threads and cotton batting, and settle into a circle to piece together a wonderful quilt for some lucky bride or new baby. We'd sing all the hymns and harmonies we knew, and indulge in an occasional break for tea and cookies. I have to admit sometimes we'd even gossip a mite — but never was a mean thing said about anyone! All the ladies prided themselves on coming up with intricate and unique patterns — everything from the traditional wedding ring design to crazy-yet-elegant patchworks with rich, dark patterns and velvets!

Why did the ladies love quilting so? Well, for one thing, it was a social outlet for folks who often spent entire weeks on housework without talking to another soul except their own husbands and youngsters. For another, each quilt represented a lasting, artistic accomplishment — something a woman could point to with pride and even hand down to the next generation. This quote from "Aunt Jane of Kentucky" helps sum it up better than I could:

"I've been a hard worker all my life, but 'most all my work has been the kind that 'perishes with the usin',' as the Bible says. That's the discouragin' thing about a woman's work. If a woman was to see all the dishes that she had to wash before she died piled up before her in one pile, she'd lie down and die right then and there. I've always had the name o' bein' a good housekeeper, but when I'm dead and gone there ain't anybody goin' to think o' the floors I've swept, and the tables I've scrubbed, and the old clothes I've patched, and the stockin's I've darned, but when one of my grandchildren or great-grandchildren see one o' these quilts, they'll think about Aunt Jane, and, wherever I am then, I'll know I ain't forgotten."

So we all got quite a bit out of our quilting bees. As life became busier though, it seems there were seldom enough free hours to hold a quilting bee anymore. But all the ladies still craved pretty quilts for their homes, for gifts, and to decorate boarding houses and inns. And that's where I came in! What with my own children grown and moved Back East, and my husband Sam Willoughby still working all day at the U.S. Post Office here in town, I needed something to keep my heart and hands busy. So I decided to open a little quilt shop here in our house, and let everyone in Liberty Falls vie for my creations! I must say it amazes me how many quilts I've completed over the years.

You say you're staying at The Wooden Nickel Inn? Why, every single quilt on the beds there is an "Aunt Alice original," designed in collaboration with the Inn's owners, Mr. and Mrs. Johnson themselves! Mrs. Applegate wouldn't think of offering "her boys" a room at the Boarding House without an Aunt Alice quilt on the bed, and all of the Clark and DuBois youngsters have been gifted with my wedding ring designs on the occasion of their nuptials! What's more I was delighted when the Ladies Temperance Society asked me to sew up a set of six matching quilts for the lodging they're offering to young single women new to Liberty Falls. I even made up some pretty ruffled curtains for the sleeping rooms as my gift to the Society! I take special orders, too — so if you'd like an all-white quilt for your summer bed or a tiny quilt for a baby's cradle, just stop by and let's talk! You'll find me here on my porch in nice weather, sewing up the quilts I've patched together inside on my dining room table.

You know, making quilts comes almost as natural to me as breathing. Why, one of my earliest childhood memories is sitting at the feet of my mother and grandmother, sorting scraps of material for the quilts they were creating. I'll never forget the yarns granny spun about the wonderful history of quilts. Whenever I hear this song called "Patchwork," I think of her with love and reverence:

> *Grannie sits in her oaken chair*
> *The firelight flits o'er her silvery hair,*
> *The silent children around her sit,*
> *As she pieces her patchwork coverlet.*
> *She tells them her story of London Town,*
> *And shows them the scraps of her bridal gown;*
> *Each fragment there is a printed page,*
> *With mem'ries written 'twixt youth and age.*

Now you know, many folks think that quilts are an American colonial invention — but nothing could be further from the truth! If you're interested, sit down here beside me for a spell and I'll "patch together" the story of quilts for you — just as my granny used to tell it to me! Meanwhile I'll keep right on with my stitching, if you don't mind — this red-and-white quilt on my lap is due to be auctioned off at the Prairie Church picnic on Sunday, so I've got to keep to my schedule!

If you know your Bible, perhaps you've heard the story of Naa-mah, a woman born in the seventh generation after Cain. Legend has it that she invented both spinning and weaving. What a clever lady! Also from ancient times, Egyptian mummies are wrapped with some wonderful textiles, similar to what we call linen, cotton and wool. Egyptians also developed their own style of embroidery, including wonderfully intricate wall hangings in many rich colors. The Psalms tell us that the Pharaoh's daughter was brought to the king in a set of clothing made of needlework, too. All these early attempts at fabric crafts led the Egyptians to create what may have been the world's first patchworks. In fact, one day when I shared this legend with Miss Adams over at the Liberty Falls Library and Reading Room she showed me a book with a picture of an Egyptian Queen's funeral tent made in a patchwork fashioned from colored goatskins!

Getting back to Christian history, it seems that in the early days of the church women were encouraged to work in the textile arts, creating colorful hangings and vestments. At one point a church bishop called for this practice to stop, fearing that his priests were more concerned with their clothing than with their calling! These early church works did not consist of patchwork, but rather of embroidery in most cases. But in the 11th century and afterward throughout the Middle Ages, both quilting and appliqué became high art forms — especially in Spain. Silk and velvet fabrics were used to create wonderful wall hangings both for religious use and for kings and nobles.

Recalling all these historic facts, I've worked with several of the clergymen here in Liberty Falls to develop handsome patchwork hangings to decorate their churches in various seasons of the year. Father Jeremiah Davies has been particularly receptive: his church boasts complete sets of hangings for both Lent and Advent! I consider designing pieces like that to be my Christian service — and once they see how beautiful the hangings can be, usually the church Ladies' Circles will take on the project of cutting and sewing the fabric.

Not to be outdone by other parts of Europe, the Scandinavian countries enjoy considerable "fabric history" of their own — particularly in Sweden. As you may know, Swedish furniture looks quite stiff and spare, but when the Swedes create lovely wall hangings and quilts, the appearance of their rooms gains wonderful color and softness, making the living areas much more inviting. Occasionally the Swedes used patchwork for their medium, but they seem to have preferred embroidery and painting during the period from the 1600s to the present.

According to my granny's tales, American quilting methods came mainly from the Dutch and English colonists — French and Spanish settlers seem to have left their needlework skills largely behind them! Perhaps this can be attributed to the areas where these various groups settled: there is not much need for a warm quilt in South and Central America, for example, where the Spaniards most often congregated. Another reason may be that both the Spaniards and French sent male explorers and settlers to the New World, with few women arriving for considerable time. Once the "fairer sex" established a presence in North America, it seems that the English and Dutch needlework arts gained prominence quite swiftly.

Imagine living in a log home in the Massachusetts winter during the 1700s. The wind whipping through the doors, windows and even the walls would have made nights particularly unbearable without an ample supply of thick and cozy bedding! What's more, according to my granny the colonists didn't stop at covering their beds with quilts and counterpanes ten-thick! They'd sew up sets of heavy, quilted curtains to cover windows and doors against the cold. Humble homes might have had these curtains made of natural fibers woven by the lady of the house herself, while grander abodes boasted silk damask curtains with matching or contrasting quilted silk lining. How elegant! Ladies soon realized that quilted garments could keep them warm during the day as well, and they'd sew up multi-layered petticoats to wear under their skirts during chilly weather.

If you think about the values of the English Puritan colonists, it will help you understand another reason why making quilts was so popular back then. "Waste not, want not" was one of the Puritans' oft-quoted virtues, so whenever a piece of clothing was too worn to keep in its present form, ladies would snip out pieces of still-good fabric and save them for their quilting fests. You may have wondered why some family patchworks contain both serviceable cottons and elegant brocades, silks and velvets. It's likely that the fancy fabrics came from men's coat linings, dress vests and other "Sunday best" items.

Aunt Alice is always delighted to show off her latest creations to Liberty Falls friends and customers.

Speaking of Sunday, that makes me think of church. I'll never forget something else "Aunt Jane of Kentucky" said about how quilt making was a great deal like life itself from the Biblical perspective:

"How much piecin' a quilt is like livin' a life! Many a time I've set and listened to Parson Page preachin' about predestination and free will, and I've said to myself, 'If I could jest git up in the pulpit with one of my quilts I could make it a heap plainer to folks than parson's makin' it with his big words.' You see, you start out with jest so much caliker; you don't go to the store and pick it out and buy it, but the neighbors will give you a piece here and a piece there, and you'll have a piece left over every time you cut a dress, and you take jest what happens to come. And that's like predestination. But when it comes to the cuttin' out, why, you're free to choose your own pattern...The Lord sends us the pieces, but we can cut them out and put 'em together pretty much to suit ourselves, and there's a heap more in the cuttin' out and the sewin' than there is in the caliker."

I was thinking about "Aunt Jane" last Sunday in church when I happened to gaze around the congregation and saw two of my favorite Liberty Falls ladies sitting nearby. They're both "kindred spirits" of mine because each lady runs her own small business from a house here in town — why, we're getting so we generate almost as much foot traffic as the storefronts on Main Street! The ladies' names are Susan Davidson and Eloise Perkins, and their businesses are "Susan's Hat Shop" and "Red Rudder Antiques"!

You know, old-timers hereabouts love to spin yarns about the early days when there were no "specialty suppliers" like Susan, Eloise and myself. The only place you could go to buy most anything for yourself or your home was Tully's General Store. Back in the 1860s, the Tullys carried it all: food, tools, housewares, and even gents' and ladies' apparel! Then the Ross Bros. Clothiers opened on Main Street, and gentlemen at last had a special place to purchase fashionable clothing for business and personal wear. A few years later Susan Ross — wife of one of the two brothers who own Ross Bros. — brought back some ladies' hats when she accompanied her man Herman on a buying trip Back East. Mrs. Ross convinced Herman and his brother Emmanuel to let her have one of the storefront windows and a corner of the store itself for her "ladies millinery department." And to "drum up" business, Susan took to wearing a different stunning hat every time she made an appearance in public!

Susan Davidson was welcomed in fancy stores like these before moving to Liberty Falls, where she used her high-class contacts to start her own fashionable hat shop.

Then Susan decided to turn her attention to ladies' ready-to-wear, leaving the door open for another Susan — the Mrs. Davidson I mentioned before — to start her own thriving hat business! Susan Davidson spent her youthful years in Europe as the daughter of an international businessman. After her marriage to a financier, she found herself transplanted to Liberty Falls some years ago. Sadly, her husband's ventures failed and he died young of a heart attack. Left on her own with limited resources, she had a brainstorm. Why not use her many European contacts to bring beautiful millinery to the ladies of Liberty Falls? Susan Ross had already proven that there was a ready market, and Mrs. Ross herself told Mrs. Davidson to "go right on ahead" since the Ross venture was now strictly clothing oriented.

Susan Davidson bought a modest home and fixed up the two front rooms as a store. Why, it was her example that first gave me the courage to do the same when I opened my quilt shop! She offers hats for just about every season, lifestyle and pocketbook as well as friendly fashion advice for the Liberty Falls ladies. "Fashion leaders" like the bankers' wives Mrs. Clark and Mrs. DuBois have been known to purchase a hat from Susan to go with every frock in their wardrobes. Those two ladies have a bit of a rivalry going, you know, when it comes to everything from their home decor to their grandchildren's grades in school! Then there are the more practical types like Mrs. Applegate of the Boarding House, the baker Clara Goodfriend, and me. We only purchase one or two "all-purpose" hats a year, but that Susan Davidson knows exactly what colors and styles will flatter us and go with most anything we wear.

Every now and again on an afternoon where my fingers get a bit tired from quilting, I'll stroll on over to Susan Davidson's and ask her to show me the latest styles from London, Paris, New York and Denver. I was just over their last week, so if you're curious, I'll share some of the "fashion secrets" with you. A hat called the "Langtry," made of real seal with a grosgrain ribbon bow looked quite attractive to me, but at $11.00, I told Susan I'd pass. One called the "Russell," also made of seal, caught my eye, too — it had a pattern of feathers arranged to look like an actual bird on top! Still, at $7.75, I could hardly justify the price. I did pick up a new chiffon veil to go with my trusty Sunday bonnet. The veils came in brown, navy, green or black, and each one was just 50 cents — which I considered quite a good bargain!

On my way back from "Susan's Hat Shop," I stopped off for a spell to chat with Eloise Perkins. It's always a pleasure to visit her pretty little house because she has such a wonderful eye for fine furniture and "home touches." For years, Eloise has been one of our town's most beloved hostesses for afternoon tea and conversation. So when her husband Alfred went to his reward and Mrs. P. needed a source of income and diversion, this talented lady made her livelihood as a dealer of antiques. From the outside, her house looked just about the same except for the sign she placed on one wall reading "Red Rudder

Antiques." Yet during fine weather, there are a few "tell-tale signs" of what a visitor might discover inside. In summer, Mrs. P. decorates her tiny yard with choice selections from her wares: a handsome mirror, a set of matching storage trunks, an old butter churn, a wagon wheel, a baby rocker and such.

Even so, a visitor has to go inside to gain a glimpse of all the finest specimens. At first, Eloise got most of her inventory from folks in Liberty Falls who wanted a discreet way of gaining some extra cash. But later on she'd send for more elegant and exotic pieces to arrive by train — some were even French and English antiques to suit the expensive tastes of the bankers' wives, Doc Stevens' wife, and other well-heeled Liberty Falls society types!

Well, I really appreciate having had this opportunity to chat with you while I sewed on this quilt — as you can see, I'm nearly finished! I'll need to go inside now and start Sam's supper. But before we say good-bye, let me leave you with a thought or two that sums up my philosophy of life. It's from a poem by a lady named Elizabeth Ryan DeCoursey:

Life is like a patchwork quilt
And each little patch is a day,
Some patches are rosy, happy and bright,
And some are dark and gray.

But each little patch as it's fitted in
And sewn to keep it together
Makes a finished block in this life of ours
Filled with sun, and with rainy weather.

So let me work on Life's patchwork quilt
Through the rainy days and the sun —
Trusting that when I have finished my block
The Master may say: "Well done."

HISTORIC NAMES OF AMERICAN QUILT PATTERNS

Quilts Named After Trades and Tools

Anvil
The Ship's Wheel
Monkey Wrench
Chips and Whetstones
Brick Pile

Saw-Tooth
Carpenter's Wheel
Water Mill
The Dusty Miller

Quilts Named for Natural Things

Garden Maze
Spider Web
Ocean Wave
Unknown Star
Peonies
Mexican Rose
Pineapple Design
Big Dipper

Autumn Leaf
Rolling Stones
Flying Geese
Double Tulip
North Carolina Lily
Rose of Sharon
Charter Oak
Butterflies

Quilts With Religious and Biblical Names

Jacob's Ladder
Job's Tears
Tree of Paradise
World Without End
Cross and Crown
Star of Bethlehem

Job's Trouble
Joseph's Coat
Wonder of the World
The Cross
Garden of Eden

Quilts With Political Influences

Clay's Choice
Fifty-Four-Forty or Fight
State House Steps

Whig Rose
Lincoln's Platform
Temperance Tree

CHAPTER III

The Local Landmarks of Liberty Falls

A personal tour of Liberty Falls and Colorado historic structures...as conducted by the second mayor of this thriving town, the Honorable Mr. Willie Griffin

Welcome, my friends! Welcome to Liberty Falls! I'm the mayor, Willie Griffin at your service. We're delighted to have you here in town. In fact, ever since Leadville announced its plans to attract tourism with that opulent Ice Palace of theirs, we've been reaching out to folks all over the West and inviting them to come visit us as well! Was your train ride comfortable? Good! I'll let you get freshened up before we start and then I'll show you around town and point out some of our newer landmarks and attractions. And if you've a mind to stay a short spell longer with me, I can tell you about a few of the other famous locales elsewhere in Colorado, too! Then Mrs. Smoots will welcome you to dinner over at The Old Homestead Restaurant. Her chicken and dumplings are my favorites — and if you take a gander at my waistline, you'll see I've been indulging quite a bit lately! I'll drop you off at the restaurant once our tour is complete!

First off, let me assure you that our fair town comes by its name quite honestly. There is a natural-flowing falls in these parts, so follow me and I'll lead you right to it! You see, in the early days of our town's settlement, when Liberty Falls was nothing more than a cluster of tents for miners and the like, one lucky prospector came across these falls as he searched the countryside for signs of gold. He brought some of his fellow miners to see it, and they marveled at the falls' gentle flow, their sparkling waters, and the serene sound of the burbling water as it cascaded down the rocks.

No one quite remembers who named the town "Liberty Falls," but legend has it that a group of miners agreed on the name one night after a few drinks at the camp's first makeshift saloon. "This new land provides liberty for each of us to strike it rich — or go broke. It's all up to me — and you!" one miner is reported to have said. Then one of the more poetic among them said, "Let's name this town Liberty Falls!" The rest is history. That is unless you ask some of our more conservative churchgoers around town. They deny the "saloon connection" with the town's name and claim it was coined by early settlers from Philadelphia and Washington D.C. anxious to connect their new home to the "Cradle of Liberty" Back East.

Whatever the town name's origins, these falls have become quite the favorite spot for fun during fine weather. Folks climb up to the "Scenic Overlook," just like we're doing now. Here you can enjoy the beauty of the falls and the panorama of our gorgeous Colorado mountains. Climbers practicing for a Pike's Peak trip often limber up on these rugged rocks surrounding the falls, and when the wild blueberries are in season, ladies gather them here to make their jams, jellies and shortcakes. Now, I don't mean to alarm you, but please do keep a good watch while we're here for the bears! The local brown bears seem to consider this area a perfect site for "people watching" — and if you put your picnic basket down for more than a minute, you can expect Mama Bear and her cubs to steal it clean away! Mama Bear might seem pretty gentle, but if you approach those cubs, watch out! Enough said...let's move on, if you're ready!

While we're here on the outskirts of town, let me just point out the general direction of our local fairgrounds. We have our harvest fair there every year where the ladies compete for "biggest sunflower," "best preserves," and all manner of other homely arts. I'm often lucky enough to get to judge the food entries — another reason why my belly's so round, I'm sure! The fairgrounds also played host last summer to Greller's Family Circus. What an extravaganza! You'll have to join us next year when the Greller troupe returns! They bring a glorious Big Top tent with a bright, red-and-white striped top, more wild animals than you can shake a stick at, clowns galore, tightrope walkers — the whole circus gamut! Greller's brought a little carousel with them and we were so inspired by it that we raised money to build our own carousel here in Liberty Falls! We ordered each of the carousel horses special from Philadelphia — the Dentzel Company makes them the best in the world, according to our former mayor Paul Johnson. He's retired now from his law practice, but he still comes downtown every day in his pin-striped suit, just to see what's going on and provide me guidance when I need it.

As we head on back into town, let me walk you through General Miles Memorial Park — a tribute to our very own Civil War hero, General Robert Miles. You know, a town as young as Liberty Falls has very few heroes to date, but General Miles makes up for that all by himself, considering his exploits. Robert Miles left the U.S. Army after 20 years of service right about 1858. He was still a fairly young man — young enough, at least, to dream of striking it rich when he heard about the Colorado Gold Rush. Miles made his way West to Colorado and was just starting to make a few dollars as a miner when he got the news that war had broken out between the North and South. This old soldier was unable to resist selling out his claims and heading Back East to see what he could do in aid of his nation. Now, Miles had never been anywhere near the rank of General when he was in the army before, but after all, that was peacetime! He was placed in charge of a regiment, did his duty with honor, and several field promotions later he was named General Miles by President Abe Lincoln himself!

After the war, General Miles came back to Liberty Falls and we locals honored him with a parade and many fine gifts. By then, most of the good claims had long since been staked, so a mining career for Robert Miles was not realistic. Because of his distinguished service, however, the General had his pick of business opportunities from admiring Liberty Falls folk. Eventually, he chose to work in the management office of the Gold King Mines — so he ended up in the mining business after all. Imagine his pride a few years later when the Memorial Park was opened: complete with his statue in full Union regalia, a wonderful fountain, handsome trees and bushes, and plenty of places for folks to rest on benches. The park has become a favorite spot for Sunday afternoon meandering, kite flying, and sitting back to reminisce about the "good old days" by our few remaining Civil War veterans. Oh, and look — there's that pesky bird that loves to perch on General Miles' hat — one spring she even built her nest there!

Now we'll pass by the beautiful white Gazebo just before we enter the town limits proper. That's becoming the favorite place here in Liberty Falls for spring and summer weddings. And our local photographer Rodger Stuart makes quite a business of taking folks' wedding pictures under the gazebo — whether they were married there or in one of our many churches downtown. In the latter case, lots of couples hire a fancy little carriage with a "Just Married" sign on the back, then proceed to the gazebo with Rodger and his equipment following right behind. Rodger still relies on his trusty mule, Sarah, to haul all his supplies including his camera and tripod, and the small tent he uses as his mobile dark room.

At other times of the week, the gazebo serves as the center for all manner of activities: musical concerts, small presentations and plays, and even the occasional political speech by yours truly. Our bankers' wives, Mrs. Clark and Mrs. DuBois, saw a gazebo like this on one of their jaunts "Back East," and had an architect design this one for

Liberty Falls. As you can see, it has plenty of columns, a bell-shaped roof, and twin curved stairways. And look at that handsome landscaping — trees and bushes galore. Every summer, the local ladies' Garden Club makes sure that the climbing roses and other flowers are kept flourishing, too!

If you take a gander over there you'll see our town Playground — another project we Town Council members helped bring to fruition in recent years. It makes a nice complement to the Skating Pond that was put in during Mayor Johnson's term — that way, we have wholesome outdoor entertainment for the youngsters all year 'round. Some of them insist on going out to the Old Swimming Hole — that little pond we passed out there a spell back. I have to admit that the water stays blissfully cool even on scorching summer days, but we Town Council members have many concerns about safety. We couldn't pass any legislation, though, because the Swimming Hole is located outside our jurisdiction. We did put up a makeshift sign that reads "Swim at Your Own Risk," and we take turns "monitoring" the Swimming Hole in the summer time — it gives us a good excuse to take a little time off from our labors! I'll never forget when the excited dog burst onto the scene out there and chased one of the children's cats up a tree! You never heard such yowling and bawling (cat and child alike!) until I got the fire department out to bring the cat back down and subdue the pup!

I prefer to see the youngsters go with their families to the Picnic Grounds we've set up in a clearing of the woods not far from here. To encourage its use, the Town Council had "Ladies" and "Gents" outdoor facilities built, and placed a park bench there for folks who don't want to sit on the ground on a blanket. Some of the boys soon built themselves a makeshift tree house in the biggest tree available, which made me realize that the picnic grounds were already a huge success!

We're now entering the Liberty Falls Town Square — and have we ever seen the building activity in this area over the past few years! First to be christened was that imposing Clock Tower over there. It's so tall, elegant and impressive that it attracts tourists and visitors from as far away as Denver! Why, I imagine some of you are here today because you saw a picture of it in a magazine or newspaper. When the Town Council decided to build the Clock Tower, we embarked on a community-wide fundraising effort. Ladies auxiliaries held bake sales and children's groups washed windows to contribute their share, while the men's lodges and fraternal orders "passed the hat." Even Snake Eye Jake offered a night's winnings from his "take" at the Gold Nugget Tavern! Several designs were considered, but in the end our choice was unanimous: this stunning brick building with elegant, rounded windows and a generous opening to hold Liberty Falls' own answer to London's "Big Ben." I'll let you take a look around on the outside, and then we'll climb up into the Clock Tower and you can see how it works!

Next, let me direct your attention to the Bell Tower across the square. It's another one of our proud achievements — but rather than have me tell you about it, let me quote another one of our citizens. I have the clipping from the newspaper right here in my vest pocket.

Here's what "Liberty Falls Daily News" editor Oliver Cummings had to say about the new Bell Tower when it was unveiled a few years back:

> *The cosmopolitan cities of the Eastern United States and Europe would be proud to call the "Liberty Falls Bell Tower" their own. Its soaring architecture makes it an imposing presence on our Main Street Square, and its six melodious tunes bring a note of musical enjoyment to each and every day in Liberty Falls. We are delighted by the sensitivity our City Fathers have shown in the design and placement of this new landmark. Located diagonally across the Square from the handsome Liberty Falls Clock Tower, and created to harmonize in design and materials, the new Bell Tower provides balance to a Town Square of ever-growing beauty and sophistication. What's more, the Bell Tower boasts attractive and appropriate surroundings: a pretty water fountain, landscaping and seasonal floral displays to make it a most inviting destination for social occasions and leisurely walks.*

While we're in the area, perhaps you'd like to toss a penny or two into the Wishing Well. It's right over there! Oh, what lavish dreams this little well inspires! It was built as a contribution to the community by the bankers, Clark and DuBois. Surrounded as you can see by pretty trees and plantings, it's become a favorite landmark and meeting place for our local citizenry. And as an extra bonus, each month the bank's custodian scoops out the "wishing money" and donates it on behalf of the townspeople to one of the local houses of worship. The churches rotate the honor month by month — a nice little bit of extra money for building maintenance or missions! Thanks, folks, for your contributions. Now don't forget to make a wish!

When you first arrived I mentioned that grandiose Ice Palace in Leadville. Now, while Liberty Falls has long been renowned as a center for gold mining, Leadville gained fame in the mid-1870s for its rich "mother lode" of silver. Since then, Liberty Falls and Leadville have enjoyed a friendly rivalry for accomplishments in architecture, the arts, and all sorts of modern advancements. Why, even the sophisticated citizens of Denver often have found Leadville a worthy rival, considering the "silver capital's" seven churches, its three-story theater, top-quality photo studio, and hotel restaurant presided over by the former chef of New York's Delmonico's Restaurant! We folks here in Liberty Falls considered it "sour grapes" when a Denver reporter warned that English playwright fellow Oscar Wilde that Leadville was "the toughest as well as the richest city in the world and that every man carried a revolver." Well sir, Wilde was not intimidated during his visit: he allowed the Leadville miners to lower him into the Matchless Mine for an underground feast which Wilde described as three courses: "whiskey, whiskey and more whiskey"!

When the silver production began to fail a few years ago in Leadville, some people feared that Molly Brown's beautiful little city might become a ghost town in short order. Of course, copper and zinc mining combined to take up the slack money-wise, but Leadville's reputation as a dynamic, trend-setting city was at stake. So to stay in the news, the town fathers decided to build a huge, Norman-style "Ice Palace" as the centerpiece of a winter carnival for 1895-96.

A few of our own local community leaders traveled to Leadville to watch the construction of the palace and observe the carnival on behalf of Liberty Falls. They returned with much enthusiasm — especially after noting that Governor Albert W. McIntire himself had appeared in Leadville for the festivities! Our local Chamber of Commerce took up a collection for supplies to build Liberty Falls' very own Ice Castle — noting that labor would be the most expensive cost since the "raw material" would be something very easy to come by in a Colorado winter: ice!

The youngsters in our local schools were asked to submit designs for the Liberty Falls Ice Castle, keeping in mind that the local version would be much smaller and less flamboyant than the one in Leadville. Why, the Leadville Palace covered five acres and included a ballroom, a 190-by-80-foot skating rink, a restaurant, and carnival displays inside! Its 325-foot-long walls were eight feet thick, too — which kept it from melting completely until the following June!

The winning castle design for Liberty Falls was submitted by a youngster in our high school, Jeffrey Taylor. It looked for all the world like a medieval castle in France, but it was built on the scale of a small cottage. Construction began in early January, as soon as temperatures ensured good freezing for the ice. More than 200 volunteers took on the various tasks of building the castle on a plot of ground right over there in our Town Square.

The first order of business was to cut some big ice blocks from our local lakes — each block no bigger than about two by three feet so they weren't too large to carry overland. The blocks were placed side by side in keeping with Jeffrey's design, and then water was drizzled over them so that they would freeze into a solid wall.

As the design took shape, other volunteers arrived to decorate the Liberty Falls Ice Castle with flags, a wooden entry door, curtains at the windows, an ice wall and simulated moat, and rugs and furniture inside. By mid-January, the castle was ready for display. On Sunday afternoon, churchgoers flocked to the Town Square in droves to walk through the Ice Castle on their way home for dinner. That local photographer I mentioned earlier, Rodger Stuart, snapped pictures for posterity, knowing that this latest example of Liberty Falls "architecture" would not last long. Realizing that the spring thaw was just around the corner, I commissioned Stuart to make a large portrait of the "building" to be placed on display at City Hall so that all would remember the creation of the Liberty Falls Ice Castle as a special moment in the history of our fair city. So let's step inside City Hall now and take a look at it!

Yes, folks, our Liberty Falls City Hall is quite the beautiful building if I do say so myself. But let me recommend to you — if you haven't done this already — to take another train ride someday soon and visit the new Colorado Capitol building in Denver! I went to the Capitol on a junket for local government officials, and I was rightly impressed, let me tell you. I found out that the 10-acre site was donated by Henry C. Brown back in 1874 when Colorado was still a territory. Excavation for the Capitol began in 1886, and as we speak, work is still going on to complete it.

The building was designed by E.E. Meyers, and it includes a total of 160 rooms. The Capitol combines many of Colorado's own materials — Gunnison granite outer walls, Ford Collins sandstone foundations, marble from Marble, Colorado for the floors and stairs, and rose onyx wainscoting from Beulah, Colorado. Formed in the sign of a Greek cross, the building measures 383 feet long by 315 wide and resembles the design of the U.S. Capitol in Washington, D.C. The dome of the Capitol is clad in copper, but speculation is already afoot that the people of Colorado would prefer to have it adorned in shimmering gold — the metal we're most famous for. In fact, I've heard tell that a group of Colorado miners are already raising the 200 ounces of gold necessary to re-adorn the dome!

Well, folks, here we are at Mrs. Smoots' door. I hope you've enjoyed your walking tour of Liberty Falls — and I know you'll fancy Mrs. Smoots' cooking! Come back and visit us again soon: there's always something new to look at or somebody interesting to meet in Liberty Falls, Colorado!

Mayor Willie Griffin's Quick Colorado Facts

Colorado: Means "red" in Spanish

State Nickname: Centennial State
(admitted to the Union in 1876)

State Motto: Nil Sine Numine
(Nothing without providence)

State Flower: White and Lavender Columbine
(Rocky Mountain Columbine)

Colorado Day: First Monday in August

State Flag: Combines the blue of Colorado skies,
the gold of Colorado metal, the white of
mountain snow, and the red of Colorado soil

Denver Nickname: "Mile High City"

Cost to Build the
State Capitol at the
turn of the century: Nearly $3,000,000

Great Seal of Colorado: The "eye of God" in a triangle,
Roman fasces, a bundle of birch
or elm rods and a battle ax.
The bundle of rods symbolizes
strength in numbers, while the ax
represents authority and leadership.
The seal also bears the state motto
and the year Colorado gained
statehood: 1876.

CHAPTER IV

The Men of Main Street, Liberty Falls

Reminiscences from some of the early "movers and shakers" of this Colorado boom town ...as told by one of Liberty Falls' most successful entrepreneurs, Benjamin Cummings

Welcome to "B. Cummings, Sign Maker!" I'm Benjamin Cummings in the flesh — and I'm glad you happened into my shop. Now as you can readily see, these days I do a far sight more than simply making signs. This here's a full-line print shop, serving just about everybody in Liberty Falls from the Ladies' Temperance Society to the traveling circus. Why, I've printed everything from wanted posters for the Federal Marshall to wedding invites for the cream of Liberty Falls society. Not to mention the fact that pretty near every business sign on Main Street is the result of my handiwork. Yessir-ree, I've made quite a name for myself in these parts. And there's nobody in town prouder of me than my own brother Oliver. Maybe you've met him? He's the editor of the "Liberty Falls Daily News," and probably the finest newspaperman in Colorado. Yep, Oliver and I are the best of

Ben Cummings and some of his Liberty Falls cronies meet for a chat at the Clark, DuBois Bank and Mint.

"Handy Andy" Malloy built many of the handsome shelves and showcases for modern Liberty Falls stores like this one.

friends these days, but it wasn't always that way. When I arrived here in Liberty Falls we were fixin' to get tangled up in what might have been the biggest brotherly altercation since Cain versus Abel!

Now if you know Oliver, you're probably aware that our family hails from Centerville, Ohio. Back there Oliver was always the apple of my father's eye. Father thought of me more like part of a peach. The pits. Mother seemed to like me all right, but she always protected me from Father's wrath instead of making me stand on my own two feet and face the music. While young Oliver was delivering newspapers and catching on at the local paper as a reporter, I was out doing mischief — why, I'm lucky Oliver didn't write me up in the paper as some sort of underage criminal! It was tough growing up in the shadow of a brother so accomplished and ambitious. Oliver was named Editor-in-Chief of the "Centerville Gazette" when he was just 24 years old. Meanwhile, at 22 I was picking up odd jobs here and there in between my brushes with the law over various gambling schemes and other questionable ventures.

Soon after Oliver's big promotion, Mother and Father called him and me into the parlor one evening

Folks couldn't get over staring when the first of these big-wheeled bicycles made their appearance on Main Street.

with important news. Father had been in correspondence with the owners of Clark, DuBois Bank & Mint in Liberty Falls, Colorado, and they wanted him to come to work for them. It seems Father had told Mr. Clark and Mr. DuBois about his "genius son" the newspaperman, and they offered to set Oliver up with his own daily paper — "Liberty Falls Daily News." Of course, since I'd done very little to carve out a career for myself, there was no such offer for the "ne'er-do-well" son. Father made some vague comment about "finding something for me to do" in Liberty Falls, but I was too proud to go along without any specific prospects. So — much to Mother's distress — I put on a bold face and announced, "You three go along to Colorado. I'll stay here in Centerville!"

I remained back in Ohio for a good three years after the family went West. With Oliver out of town, it seemed like I was free to be my own man — no longer in my brother's shadow. I had to admit that printer's ink was in my blood, too — so I went to work for Mr. Schuler at the "Centerville Gazette" just like my brother before me. I started at the bottom — cleaning out the print shop, distributing papers to the newsboys, doing whatever needed done. Before long Mr. Schuler trusted me to begin learning how to set type and use the printing press. And by the time two years were up I was running the whole back shop of the "Gazette" — Mr. Schuler was quick to praise and reward another good employee you see, just like he had been with my brother Oliver.

All this while I wrote letters to Mother quite regularly, telling her of my progress and how I'd pretty much stayed on the "straight and narrow." She'd write back bursting with pride about how Oliver was doing so well with the "Daily News," and how Father was practically "printing money" at the bank — what with all the mining cash and construction going on in Liberty Falls. With each letter, Mother would more or less beg me to join the rest of the Cummings clan, but I was stubborn. I didn't want to play second fiddle to Oliver again, and I didn't want to have to listen to Father's stern criticism day in and day out. One day, however, I went to the Post Office and retrieved a letter in Father's handwriting. I ripped it open, fearing bad news about Mother. Thank the Lord, it was nothing like that. Here's what Father's letter said:

Dear Son,

    For months now, I've been in correspondence with my old friend Mr. Schuler at the "Centerville Gazette." He's told me about how you're a changed man: getting to work on time each morning and staying around late to make sure everything's ship-shape before you leave at night. No one remembers better than Mr. Schuler what a rabble-rouser you used to be…but that's all water under the bridge now, son, and it's not why I'm writing you this letter.

    It was always easier for me to deal with Oliver than with you, Benjamin. Oliver is so much like me, and you're more like your mother. I know now that the way I played favorites with Oliver over you was unfair — and it probably contributed to your "wild streak" and the trouble you got into as a youngster.

    These last few years on your own in Centerville were the best training in the "school of hard knocks" a man could ask for. You've stood on your own two feet, supported yourself, stayed out of trouble and made a good name for yourself with the pillars of the community. I congratulate you son, and now I have a serious request.

    Your mother and I are getting on in years, and we don't know how long we'll be around yet. I see how your mother pines for you, and I know how much it would mean to her if we were all together again in the same town. So here's my proposition. If you agree to move here to Liberty Falls, I agree to treat you as an adult worthy of respect and man-to-man friendship. And I know a young gent of your accomplishments can't help but succeed in the new land of Colorado. Why, the sky's the limit here…

Father went on and on in his letter — so unlike him! He was usually a man of few words. I could tell that he was sincere…that he wanted to make sure I understood that it would be different between the two of us in Liberty Falls. So I settled things with Mr. Schuler and helped him find a suitable replacement. I checked out of my rooming house, packed a few belongings, and jumped on the Westbound train toward Colorado.

It took me nearly a week to get to Liberty Falls — what with all the train changes and delays — but when I arrived it was worth all the time and discomfort. The look of joy on Mother's face was so glorious I almost cried. And Father greeted me with a warm handshake, looked me right in the eye and said, "Welcome, Benjamin! Welcome to Liberty Falls!" The only fly in the ointment was the greeting I got from Oliver. It seems that he was having a hard time accepting my new status as "successful son" — and while he'd never admit it, I think he was a tad jealous.

I didn't get the full sense of Oliver's wrath until I took him aside and brought him up to date on what I'd been doing at the "Centerville Gazette." You see, I'd just assumed that Oliver was of the same mind as Father: that he'd treat me as an equal now instead of a pesky kid brother. How wrong I was! Innocently, I proposed to Oliver that I take over the same job for him at the "Daily News" that I'd done back in Centerville. I could handle the printing and distribution end of the business, and Oliver could stay in charge of the editorial side. But Oliver would have none of it! Harsh words were exchanged, and for a minute or two I thought I was a 10-year-old back in Centerville, getting ready for a fist fight with my brother in the backyard of our home.

Not wanting to upset Mother and Father, we each went our own way to nurse our grievances, smoke our pipes and think. A few hours later, Oliver came knocking at the door of the guest bedroom Mother had fixed up for me. He looked a bit sheepish. No apology, but he did hold out an olive branch — or would that be an "Oliver branch" in this case?

"Ben, how about this for a compromise? Why don't you start a print shop, making handbills and signs and the like. I promise not to compete with you, and I'll even give you my overflow printing for the 'Daily News.'" I recognized that as the most magnanimous gesture I was likely to get from my proud older brother, so I shook his hand and agreed. I'd saved a few dollars in Centerville, and between that and a small loan Father arranged down at the bank, I was set up in a small storefront within a matter of weeks. What with all the fledgling businesses, government buildings, churches and other new construction in town, it seemed that just about everybody needed a sign or two made. So before long I was "in the chips" enough to move into this house I had designed and built with the help of my new friend "Handy Andy" Malloy. Over there are my living quarters, and this end combines my sign painting and print studio. The first folks to visit me here when I moved in were Oliver and his bride, followed soon after by Mother and Father. They all seem mighty proud of this "black sheep" made good — and I aim to keep in their good graces!

"Handy Andy" did a fine job on this place of mine — I'd recommend him to you if you need anything built or repaired. Andy told me he came here originally at the behest of Mr. Clark and Mr. DuBois — just like my father and brother did. It seems those rich bankers wanted Andy and other skilled carpenters to work on their houses. And the Clark and DuBois mansions are indeed two of the fanciest homes in Liberty Falls. I have to hand it to good old Andy — unlike me, he never indulged a wild streak. Even though he was single when he came here to Liberty Falls, he spent his free time helping out at the First Prairie Church.

Wouldn't you know, one Sunday morning in church, the local schoolmarm Abigail Martin introduced Andy to a pretty Liberty Falls lass named Sally Smith — younger sister to Miss Martin's all-time star pupil Jonathan. It was love at first sight, and before long "Handy Andy" was building a cozy little cottage for himself and his new bride Sally. To make sure he'd have year-round work in town, Andy hung out his shingle as "Andrew Malloy, Handyman and Painter." Between jobs building homes and offices like mine, work at City Hall and other public buildings, Andy makes himself a good living. And he even saves time to do some fix-up chores around his own home — much to Sally's delight!

You know, my job is truly fascinating because I keep up with all the new advancements — I'm the one who prints up the handbills for just about everything that's going to be sold in these parts! Just yesterday I turned out some mighty handsome ads for the new Edison phonograph, which they call "The acme of realism." Of course, you can also still get music boxes of all types — an ad I did for Jacot & Son of New York said they run from 40 cents to $1,500! I've done some printing of ads lately for the newest in sanitary plumbing: what they call water closets and such. It won't be long before the outhouse is a thing of the past — even here in the wilds of Colorado!

Some of my favorite advertisements are for the various styles of bicycles getting popular today. The ladies who ride them look for all the world like Charles Dana Gibson's famous "Gibson Girls." Some of the more religious among us are up in arms about the fact that in order to ride a bicycle, a lady must raise her skirts as much as two inches above the ankle! These folks think that if a bachelor like me sees a lady's ankle, both she and I are about to be doomed to perdition! I've even printed some pictures of those new-fangled "horseless carriages" — European ones from Daimler and Benz, and American ones by Charles and Frank Duryea.

I've been doing quite a bit of work these days for Douglas Howard, another new friend of mine and owner of Howard's Hardware. Douglas believes strongly in advertising — and he not only places ads regularly in Oliver's newspaper, but he also prints many handbills in my shop. One day I got to talking to Douglas, and he told me about how he first came West to try to "strike it rich" in the mines some years ago. Douglas was not one of the lucky ones — he never found gold — or silver, for that matter. All he could do was catch on at the Gold King Mines, working sunup to sundown for an hourly wage. After some years of this, he was just about to pack up and head Back East when he struck up a friendship with good old Jason DuBois. These bankers certainly have had an impact on many of our lives here in town!

DuBois and Howard saw each other fairly often at meetings of the '59ers Club — a men's group for early settlers of Colorado. One day Mr. DuBois says to Douglas, "It's no secret that you'd like to leave the mining trade. If you could do anything you want instead, what would it be?" Douglas Howard didn't hesitate. "I'd run a hardware store like the ones Back East…with building supplies and tools and everything a man needs to run a ranch or home." DuBois thought that was a splendid idea — and lent his friend the money to start "Howard's Hardware" — one of Liberty Falls' thriving businesses.

One day Douglas Howard invited me to tour his building, and I was mightily impressed! I already knew about the first floor — with its 20-

foot ceilings decorated with fancy pierced copper patterns and its floor-to-ceiling shelving on one side and drawers on the other. The hardware store has fine wooden flooring, and a good 15 different glass-topped counters and displays holding everything from nuts, bolts and nails to — well, see for yourself! Here's the list I printed up for Douglas recently on his letterhead:

HOWARD'S HARDWARE
431 Main Street
Liberty Falls, Colorado

Wholesalers and Distributors
Established 1871

Kerosene Lighting
Porcelain Ware
Cast Iron Cookware
Tinware
Galvanized Ware
Steel Pipe and Fittings
Plumbing Supplies
Construction — Railroad Tools
Sledges-Bars-Diggers
Shovels-Mauls-Wedges
Axes-Picks-Mattock
Ladders-Wood-Alum
Replacement Wood Handles
Chain-Chain Fittings
Nikes-Spikes-Staples
Nuts-Bolts-Fasteners
Rope-Manila
Gold Pans
Screw-Lag-Wood-Metal
Hardware Cloth-Screen
Eyebolts-Turnbuckles
Cable-Wire-Wire Rope
Janitorial Supplies
Saws-Carpenter-Bow-Crosscut

I printed all this in small type down the left-hand side of the letter-head — otherwise there wouldn't have been any room left to write anything! The store is packed to the gills, too — but beautifully organized what with all those drawers and shelves Handy Andy built for Douglas. I especially like the touches Douglas has added: stuffed birds and animal heads for decor — it helps attract the gents to visit the hardware store on a regular basis. Upstairs there's living space for the Howard family as well as some small offices Douglas rents to doctors, lawyers and other professionals and business types. Yessir-ree, that Douglas Howard has really made a success for himself!

Of course, I'm not complaining — my shop is always bustling and there's plenty for visitors to take a look at here, too. I've got the latest wanted posters and handbills hanging up all around the shop — partly as a public service and partly so folks can see the whole range of what I can print for them. Out front I've got my solid oak counter — that's where people step up to place their orders. Back here I have trays and trays of type ready for setting, and if you like you can pick out your own paper and watch me do the printing, too! I've been playing around with this new-fangled typewriter to see if it can save me some time. Take a look! It's called a Blickensderfer and it's the latest thing!

I predict that before long many of the offices hereabouts will have their own typewriters — but I'm not worried about my business — there will still be a need for type set in various sizes and pictures on posters and such. I'll be printing in two colors before long — I've been reading about how some of the magazines are starting to experiment with red and black on white. Then I'll wager we'll figure out a way to print in full color — and after that, the sky's the limit! Why, that's exactly what father told me life would be like here in Colorado: open horizons for scenery and for a man's ambitions. It's sure worked out that way for me! Now I'll have to leave you. I'm putting the "Closed for Lunch" sign out on the door and meeting Oliver at the Old Homestead Restaurant for pot roast. That's right, we're best of friends now — and Mother couldn't be more pleased! See you when I get back!

NAMES FOR MINES — ALREADY TAKEN

B. Cummings kept this list tacked up in his shop so in case a miner came in to print up a sign for his new claim, he could check and make sure his chosen name was original. Years later, the list stayed up as something of a conversation piece, as visitors considered what would possess a miner to choose some of these unusual names! Ben also loved to tell the story about the "Bobtail Mine" in Central City. It seems a very proper lady could not bring herself to say its name, so she referred to it instead, as "Robert Appendage Mine."

Optimistic Mine Names

Golden Rule	Revenue
Little Tycoon	Coming Wonder
Miser's Dream	Smile of Fortune
U.S. Bank	Cracker Jack
Silent Friend	Sleeping Pet
Royal Flush	Hidden Treasure
Lucky Strike	

Pessimistic Mine Names

Aftermath	Neglected
Slip Up	Careless Boy
Little Fraud	Lost Trail
Flat Broke	Ground Hog
Busted Nugget	

Unfathomable Mine Names

Resurrection	Lackawanna
The Bloated Notary	Butterfly-Terrible
Spring Chicken	Pie Plant
Old Hundred	Lion's Roost
Inter-Ocean	Kreutzer Sonata

CHAPTER V

Ist Das Nicht Eine Schnitzelbank?

How Deutschlanders helped build the quality of life in America...as told by Liberty Falls' beloved German brewmeister, Joshua Ausberg

D o you know the song about the schnitzelbank? That's German for workbench — and my mother used to sing it to me every night when I was just a little snickerdoodle of a boy back in Deutschland! The song is mostly nonsense, but it still runs through my head from time to time when I'm reminiscing about my wonderful life — both back in the Old Country and now in America!

Mr. Ausberg's tireless workers "rack off" the beer at Ausberg's Brewery.

Allow me to introduce myself. I'm Joshua Ausberg, and for some years now my wife Ella and I have been running our own Ausberg's Brewery here in Liberty Falls. As you may have heard, our first venture in Liberty Falls was the poor old Blue Whale Tavern. Alas, it burned down in the middle of the night many years ago — just as I was

Here's a glimpse at how lager beer is manufactured at Ausberg's and Coors'.

planning to upgrade it into one of those elegant establishments like they have in Denver and Kansas City. Mirrors, carved bar, brass rails and spittoons, and a velvet-curtained stage for entertainment! It would have been glorious! But before I could rebuild, I heard about several new competitors coming into town, so Ella and I decided to indulge my life-long dream: opening up our very own brewery.

Now of course, not just any herr and frau can start and run a successful brewery. But luckily for Ella and me, I began brewing beer not much after I learned to tie my own shoes! Have you heard of that fine gentleman Adolph Coors over in Golden? Why, Adolph and I both apprenticed together for John Stenger's brewery in Naperville, Illinois. That wasn't long after Adolph and I came to America — our families both arrived on these shores right after the Civil War. When I left Stenger's, I lost track of Adolph until 1873, at which point I happened to pick up a newspaper from Golden while riding on the train. I'll never forget my excitement when I saw this item in the November 12, 1873 issue of the "Colorado Transcript:"

> *"Another new and extensive manufactury is about to be added to the number already in Golden. Messers. J. Scheuler and Adolph Coors, of Denver, have purchased the old tannery property of C.C. Welch and John Pipe, and will convert it into a brewery. They propose making large additions to the building, making it into one of the most extensive works of the kind in the territory, completing it about the first of February. We welcome these energetic men among us, and trust they will be as successful as they anticipate."*

When I got home I dropped Adolph a letter by way of General Delivery, Golden, Colorado, congratulating him on his new business and reintroducing myself. Much to my delight, he sent Ella and me an invitation to the grand opening that February. I confess that on seeing the Coors Brewery, my feelings of happiness for Adolph were mixed with a bit of envy. Oh, the familiar sour-sweet smell of the grains and hops! The shine of the copper equipment, imported from our native Germany! The pride of Adolph as he showed me his distinctive new label!

I was so inspired that by the time Adolph invited Ella and me back to Golden for his marriage on April 12, 1879, our own Ausberg's Brewery was up and running. Adolph's small but elegant wedding was the talk of Colorado society, as the "Transcript" indicated:

"But few of the many friends of Mr. Adolph Coors, the popular and successful brewer, were aware of the intended marriage. It occurred, however, at the residence house on the brewery grounds last Saturday evening, April 12, in the presence of a small circle of his immediate friends. Mr. and Mrs. Hauptman, parents of the bride, Miss Louisa M. Weber, witnessed the ceremony which was performed in a graceful and impressive manner by Judge A.D. Jameson. The Transcript joins a large circle of admirers in Golden, Denver, and throughout the state, in wishing Mr. and Mrs. Coors a happy journey through life, with mile-stones of the incidental blessings that wait on matrimony."

The happy couple made their home in what once was a dance pavilion, converted to their use and renovated over the years to fit the needs of their growing family. And just as the Coors' fortunes grew, so did the Ausbergs'. Yes, Ella and I found that Liberty Falls has its own wonderful source of mountain spring water, just like Golden. It's as pure as the water from the Rhine country of Germany where Adolph and I come from originally. Having so much in common, to this day Adolph and I correspond and visit whenever we can. As fellow brewers, we dream up lots of ideas that both of us can use. For instance, we both have the following three policies in effect for the operation of our breweries:

- Fair pay and fair treatment of the men who work here

- Devotion of long hours of hard work to improve the quality of the product

- Foregoing personal luxury and pleasures for the expansion and improvement of the plant

We also spend time coming up with extra ways to make money. For example, both Coors and Ausberg's offer regular ice wagon service to our towns, and we both keep barley seed for sale to local farmers. In recent years we've worked together to help combat the effects of the Women's Christian Temperance Union and other prohibitionists. You may have heard about that movement here in Liberty Falls and how some of the ladies are trying to get everyone over the age of three to "take the pledge"! Lucky for both Adolph and me, our own workers are mostly churchgoers and pillars of the local communities. They're the most wholesome advertisements against prohibition any brewer ever could want.

Adolph and I indulged in some friendly competition at the Chicago World's Fair in 1893 — we both were invited to compete among 25 American breweries and sundry foreign entries for "best beer" prizes. While our beer received some fine compliments, Adolph walked off with one of the American awards — the only winner with a brewery West of the Missouri River! His success (and mine) certainly fills us with pride and satisfaction, considering our humble origins as German immigrants!

Ah, yes...the Coors and Ausberg families were among the many, many thousands of Germans to leave Deutschland for North America over the past two centuries. Even today, Ellis Island in New York accepts boat after boat of prospective citizens hoping to find a better life in the New World. I've only seen the Statue of Liberty in pictures, but I can imagine the rising excitement of an immigrant family as their boat steams in to New York Harbor in full view of that welcoming 152-foot lady with the torch! Of course, "Miss Liberty" wasn't there yet when my family arrived in the 1860s — she was a gift from the French people to celebrate 100 years of independence for the United States of America!

You probably all know at least part of the poem Emma Lazarus wrote to appear on the statue's 150-foot pedestal:

The New Colossus

Not like the brazen giant of Greek fame,
With conquering limbs astride from land to land,
Here at our sea-washed, sunset gates shall stand
A mighty woman with a torch, whose flame
Is the imprisoned lightning, and her name
Mother of Exiles. From her beacon-hand
Glows world-wide welcome; her mild eyes command
The air-bridged harbor that twin cities frame.

"Keep ancient lands, your storied pomp!" cries she
With silent lips. "Give me your tired, your poor,
Your huddled masses yearning to breathe free,
The wretched refuse of your teeming shore.
Send these, the homeless, tempest-tost to me,
I lift my lamp beside the golden door!"

Indeed, the United States appeared to offer a "golden door" of opportunity for so many of us Germans as well as immigrants from countries all over Europe. Over the generations, whenever Germany encountered religious strife, war, or economic peril, America has beckoned.

Of course, the Germans have never been known as natural explorers. After all, most of our states are land locked! But our history books tell us that a German named Tyrker actually accompanied Leif Ericson on his voyage to Newfoundland about 1,000 years ago! Germans also went along with the French Huguenots to Florida, with Captain John Smith to Jamestown, Virginia, and with the Dutch to "New Amsterdam" — now known as New York. Historians also believe that it was the German mapmaker Martin Waldseemueller who came up with the name "America" in the first place. He read the accounts of Amerigo Vespucci's travels, and dubbed the new territory in honor of the famed explorer.

According to what I learned in my studies for American citizenship, the first Germans to come to the colonies probably arrived in the late 1600s. They were fleeing the devastation of the Thirty Year War, which resulted from Martin Luther's defection from the Catholic Church 100 years earlier. Imagine this: during that war, between 1618 and 1648, more than half of the German population died!

The original German version of the "Mayflower" was called the "Concord," and it arrived on these shores in 1683, holding 13 families led by Francis Daniel Pastorius. These were the original founders of Germantown, Pennsylvania. William Penn, for whom Pennsylvania was named, could not have been more delighted to see the Germans arrive. Penn did everything he could to encourage more German immigration, and by 1745 there were 45,000 Deutschlanders in

Pennsylvania. Why, by 1766, one-third of the population of Pennsylvania was German!

Maybe you've heard the story about how the Pennsylvania Deutsch started being called "Pennsylvania Dutch"? When many of these folks arrived in America, they were asked their nationality. When they said Deutsch, which means "German," the English-speaking officials often misunderstood and put down "Dutch." Thus the conservative German Amish folk who clustered around Lancaster, Pennsylvania even today are called "Pennsylvania Dutch."

These so called "Dutch" became famous for the invention of the Conestoga Wagon — a freight carrying vehicle they named for the creek with the name of the Conestoga Indians. Eventually these sturdy wagons were used to help families move West — but they originally served as supply wagons during the Revolutionary War. Each complete wagon was about 26 feet long by 11 feet wide and weighed 3,000 pounds. Pulled by six horses, each wagon could haul two to three tons of supplies at a time! You'd know one if you saw it: these are the wagons with the big curved tops covered with white homespun or canvas.

Speaking of the Revolution, many of the new German immigrants jumped right in to help defend Liberty. Even though they couldn't speak English, no matter: some of their leaders were Germans, too — and there were sufficient bilingual soldiers around to translate. Famous German leaders on the colonial side included Peter Muhlenberg, Baron DeKalb, and Baron Friedrich Wilhelm von Steuben. Also — did you ever hear of "Molly Pitcher," who fired her own cannon in the Battle of Monmouth after her husband fell injured? Molly's real name was Maria Ludwig, and she was the daughter of German immigrants!

Yes, there were plenty of us who made news in America way back then. Christian Priber came to South Carolina from Germany in the 1730s, and tried to convince the Indians and white men living West of the Smoky Mountains to follow him on a quest for Utopia. Unfortunately for Priber, the English and French considered him a threat and had him imprisoned for the rest of his life! Happier stories belong to a number of German gents who marked "firsts" in the United States. For example, William Rittinghausen started the country's first papermill, in Germantown, PA. Caspar Wistar founded the glassmaking industry in America, and Henry William Stiegel made rare colored glass in Manheim, PA. Christopher Saur published the first Bible in the American colonies, printed in the German language. He also started the country's first religious magazine. His son later founded the nation's first foundry for making moveable type.

Who could forget that impressive mogul John Jacob Astor? He was a German, too! One of American history's most famous self-made businessmen, he came to this land at the age of 20 and soon was trading in furs and musical instruments. Between his fur business, his real estate holdings, and many other ventures, he became the richest man in America. At his death, he was worth $20,000,000!

Of course, these famous types were only a few of the Germans who made their way to America. After the Revolution, immigration picked up even more. In fact, American businessmen started traveling to Germany in the 1800s to recruit workers for their growing industrial economy. Even though German craftsmen often were forbidden to leave Germany, they found ways to do so. Why, one fellow even sneaked out by having himself shipped on a boat as a corpse in a coffin! This list I just picked up from the local Library and Reading Room shows how many Germans came to America in each of the decades of this last century:

1820	968
1821-1830	6,761
1831-1840	152,454
1841-1850	434,626
1851-1860	951,667
1861-1870	787,468
1871-1880	718,182
1881-1890	1,452,970
1891-1900	505,152

People with specific skills gravitated to the cities, while unskilled laborers went to rural areas and worked as farmers. As they had during the Revolutionary War, many German immigrants joined the cause of the Civil War — on the Union side. There were entire battalions of German-speaking soldiers, led by German-speaking officers! Of course, many of us Germans eventually moved West — some in "colonies" to form our own towns. Why, there are actually some of these colonies near Liberty Falls. And in Denver, you can hardly miss the several German neighborhoods with their social clubs, churches and beer gardens!

We even have our own little "colony" here in Liberty Falls — what with John Strauss who works for the railroad, Stu Bergman of Bergman's Clock Shop, and my good friend Chester Berghoff, owner of the local butcher shop. Strauss has been here in Liberty Falls the longest of all of us — why, his family came West in their own Conestoga wagon when John was just a boy. The Bergmans got here more recently — struck by the opportunity to open a specialized store in the booming town of Liberty Falls.

As you can imagine, years ago this little mining town had to rely mostly on what folks could get at Tully's General Store. But as Liberty Falls grew and developed, we've had a real boom in construction on Main Street. We enjoy retail ventures now for everything from ladies' hats to gents' clothing to hardwares, quilts, and feed and grain. If you want to visit Stu Bergman's clock shop, just locate our downtown Clock Tower. Stu's store is right across the street. Each day as the Clock Tower chimes out the passing hours, Stu welcomes customers to view his unrivaled selection of Swiss pocket watches as well as clocks of all descriptions.

No request for a timepiece is ever too humble or too grand for Stu to fulfill: he supplies simple wood-cased clocks for the miners and ranch hands as well as graceful brass models for ladies' sitting rooms. Why, Ella loves the one I got her for Christmas last year. Speaking of Christmas, the Bergmans, Strausses, Berghoffs and we Ausbergs have introduced all of Liberty Falls to our favorite German holiday traditions. In fact, most folks agree it was we Germans who set the tone for America's Christmas celebration! Back in the Old Country, we decorated fir trees and sang wonderful carols like "Silent Night." And it seems our friends from many other lands enjoy these traditions as well. Here are the words to "Silent Night" in German, written by Joseph Mohr (1792-1848) and put to music by Franz Xaver Gruber (1787-1863):

Stille Nacht

Stille Nacht, heilige Nacht.
Alles scläft, ein sam wacht.
Nur das traute hoch heilige Paar.
Holder Knabe im lokkigen Haar,
Schlaf in himmlischer Ruh,
Sclaf in himmlischer Ruh!

As for the Berghoff Butcher Shop, it seems that Chester did his apprenticeship just down the road from where I did mine in Naperville. Yes, Chester grew up in the Stockyards neighborhood of Chicago, and was apprenticed as a butcher before his 14th birthday. Chester could have enjoyed a secure and predictable life in Chicago, but his boyhood readings made him anxious to see the Wild West for himself. As a young man he boarded the train for Liberty Falls with all his worldly goods in two small bags and a knapsack. Two decades later, the Berghoff Butcher Shop reigns as one of our town's most successful small businesses. And while Chester soon learned that the West wasn't always so "wild" after all, he found himself enchanted by the mountains, valleys, and wide-open spaces of his new home.

Back in Chicago, Chester spent most of his time butchering hogs and cows with the occasional lamb and sometimes poultry. In Liberty Falls, his talents soon were tested when the locals brought in wild game as well. Before long, Chester mastered the art of butchering deer and buffalo, and of dressing pheasants and other game birds that would make their appearance "at table." His shop bustles all day long with private customers as well as errand boys picking up orders for our local restaurants and hotels.

Yes, we German-Americans have come a long way from our cold-water flats in the tenements of New York. Thanks to our successful apprenticeships and the "can-do" attitudes of folks in our adopted land, our future is bright indeed. And nowhere is it brighter than in Liberty Falls, Colorado!

MR. AUSBERG'S QUICK LIST OF "AMERICAN" WORDS WITH GERMAN ORIGINS

As we Germans have taken up residence in the United States, we've gifted American citizens with some of our descriptive and colorful language. Here are a few of the words you probably use every day that came originally from my language:

delicatessen	dumb	frankfurter	gesundheit
hausfrau	kindergarten	liverwurst	nix
noodles	ouch	pretzel	pumpernickel
sauerkraut	schnitzel	wanderlust	wieners
ya	zwieback		

MR. BERGHOFF THE BUTCHER'S TIPS FOR MEAT LOVERS

Over my years as a butcher, here are some of the less-known tips you hunters and cooks might enjoy knowing and using:

- The liver of a young deer tastes very much like veal. You can cut it in thin slices and then fry or broil it as you prefer.

- The best animal for beef is a steer that is at least 2-1/2 years old. Keep it in a stall or small pen and feed it corn for the last month or two of its life.

- Hogs may be stunned before killing and butchering, just as cattle are, but it is easier and faster to shoot a hog between the eyes with a .22 rifle or pistol.

- A good butcher wastes nothing from the hog. Save the blood and add a handful of salt and later on you can make bloodwurst. The meat from the head and snout can be used for making head cheese.

- If ever in doubt about the quality or freshness of a piece of meat, discard it. Even a small amount of meat that is spoiled, dirty or dry will spoil a whole batch of ground meat.

- If you are only killing a few chickens at a time, I recommend dry picking of feathers. It yields a better-looking bird. The alternative is to scald the bird and pick the feathers wet, which makes them easier to remove.

- While most experts recommend that you butcher only young rabbits — no older than six months — we Germans know that even an older hare will make good hasenpfeffer.

- Have you ever tried hunting and eating woodchuck? They're among the cleanest animals, because they only eat grass, clover and alfalfa. You must remove the little dark gland behind each of the woodchuck's front legs — if it is left there the meat will have poor flavor.

- Never butcher a billy goat. The taste and smell of adult male goat meat is so bad that it's not worth the work.

MRS. ELLA AUSBERG'S RECIPE FOR "SOUR" BEER BREAD

Back in the Old Country, brewers often would save a little bit of the "spent grain" from their mash to create a nice beer bread. If you'd like to try this for yourself, just stop by our brewery and I'll give you some grain. Or, you can use this easier recipe where you simply add some beer as you're making the bread.

Ingredients for starter:
2/3 cup water
2/3 cup whole wheat flour
active dry yeast — just a pinch

Ingredients for bread:

1/4 cup of water — make sure it's warm
2 packages active dry yeast
1/2 cup beer — also warm
3-1/2 cups bread flour
kosher salt — about a tablespoon or so

Mix up your starter about a day before you want to make the bread, cover it, and set it aside. When you're ready to make bread, put the warm water in a nice big bowl and sprinkle the yeast over it. Set this aside for awhile. Then put the starter and the warm beer into your mixer bowl — one fitted with a dough hook if you've got that kind of new-fangled equipment. Stir it up a little bit. Add about 1-1/4 cups of the flour and mix until it's blended for a couple of minutes or so. Add the yeast mixture and mix again for about five minutes. Finally, add the extra flour and salt, and when you mix again you'll get something of dough consistency.

Next you're going to knead the dough for about 10 minutes on a lightly floured board. Let it rise until it doubles in size, just like you would any other bread, in a covered, oiled bowl in a warm place. When you turn it out, shape it into a round loaf and put it in a floured basket or bowl. This time when you let it rise, it should get to a little more than twice its original size. Bake this loaf at 450°F, but before you put it onto your baking sheet, score the top with a sharp knife. In your oven, you should put a roasting pan full of boiling water underneath the shelf where your bread goes. Bake for 10 minutes this way, and remove the water. Turn the temperature down to 400°F, and bake about 35-45 minutes until brown.

Many a Liberty Falls family made their way West in Conestoga wagons like these.

CHAPTER VI

Adrienne's Circus Adventures

A Liberty Falls youngster's quest to run away and join the circus... as told by one of Abigail Martin's brightest pupils, Adrienne Hook

All I ever wanted was a little excitement! Something to look forward to other than the endless round of cooking, cleaning and sewing endured by most of the grown-up Liberty Falls ladies I knew. I wanted a life of my own! I wanted to visit big cities and small towns...wear a fancy costume and swing from a trapeze like the girls I saw when the circus came to Liberty Falls!

You would have thought I'd suggested jumping off a Colorado mountain top — considering how riled up Father got that day when

Adrienne marveled at dazzling circus pictures like this in the books she borrowed from the Liberty Falls Library and Reading Room.

I offered my innocent statement at the supper table. Father was talking to my brother Eric about how Eric could go to law school and become an attorney some day. As usual, nothing special was suggested in the way of a career for me — even though I earn "all As" every marking period at the Liberty Falls Middle School! Father and Mother both assumed I'd marry young like they did, and become a full-time wife and mother. That was not my plan!

When there was a lull in the conversation, I couldn't resist making a remark. "When I get a little older, I'm going to join the circus," I commented mildly between bites of Mother's tasty beef stew. Father dropped his fork and started blustering. I could almost see smoke coming out of his ears and his face grew as red as Mother's cherry preserves. "Stop that frivolous talk this instant, young lady!" he bellowed. "No daughter of mine will ever come within 50 feet of those raucous circus types — let alone join them on their aimless trips through the West. Tamera, I told you we should never have let these children go to the circus!"

If it hadn't been for Mother, Eric and I never would have seen the circus at all — but she herself was caught up in the romance of it all. From the time Mayor Willie Griffin first broached the subject of bringing a circus to Liberty Falls, it had been the talk of all the men's lodges and ladies' sewing circles. Folks looked forward to the circus with great anticipation of all the colorful costumes, funny clowns, handsome carousel horses, wild animal acts, calliope music and good things to eat. But there was a bit of fear mixed in with their excitement. Circus people were thought to be wild and unpredictable...characteristics not normally seen in folks around Liberty Falls. And now, Father's greatest fears about the circus seemed confirmed. His innocent little daughter (me!) had been captivated by the lure of the Big Top!

How well I remember that wintry night last year when Father came home from the Town Council meeting harrumphing and blustering for all he was worth. "Mayor Griffin has taken the fool notion that we need more entertainment in these parts," he bellowed as he brushed the snow off his caped winter overcoat and handed his top hat to Mother. "As if hymn-singing on Sundays isn't enough excitement for any God-fearing citizen! Those puppet Councilmen all just fell right in line with him — especially when Greller the pharmacist popped up and announced that his brother Pete has his own traveling circus. 'Greller's Family Circus Big Top' they call it, and before you could say 'do tell,' the Council passed a resolution to send a telegram to Peter Greller at his winter headquarters Down South!"

Mother "tsk, tsked" right along with Father, but I could see a bright light in her eyes as she questioned Father about the meeting. "So the Circus will be coming to Liberty Falls next summer?" she asked hopefully. "Now Tamera, don't jump to conclusions. But if Greller has his way, there'll be everything from elephants to wild tigers traipsing down Main Street before you can say "Jimmy Crack Corn"!

The next morning in school, I asked my favorite teacher, Miss Abigail Martin, if she had any pictures of circuses. "Well, Adrienne," she replied thoughtfully, biting her lip and furrowing her brow," not right here at school. But how about if you and I stop over at the Library and Reading Room this afternoon and see what Miss Adams has on the shelf. It'll give me a chance to show you how to do research in a full-fledged library." That day I went home with my book strap full of wonderful volumes all about the history of the circus, circus animals and vehicles, trapeze acts, clowns, and much more! I showed my treasures to Eric, but as usual he wanted none of any extra book-learning. "Just mark the best pictures for me — especially anything with two heads from a side show," he called as he ran out the door to make snowballs with his friends.

I curled up by the parlor fireplace and read book after book about the circus. The first thing I learned was that there have been circuses all over the world for hundreds of years! In Egypt, explorers have found wall paintings they say date back to 2500 B.C., showing acrobats and the like. A couple of hundred years later, records show that the little Pharaoh Pepi II — a boy about my age — asked to see the performance of a dancing Sudanese dwarf in fancy costume. Around 300 B.C. in Egypt there was a circus-type parade of wagons and chariots and animals that lasted a whole day!

Meanwhile in China, every dynasty cooked up its own version of a circus entertainment. The Chou dynasty was partial to clowns and jesters, and the Han dynasty liked jugglers and balancing acts. The T'ang dynasty actually set up a circus school to teach young people how to become acrobats and jugglers. The Sung dynasty was partial to jugglers, too — but they expected folks to juggle with their feet!

Even the Ancient Greeks staged acts that sound a lot like what we enjoy today — featuring feats of daring and animals and such. Homer's Iliad and Odyssey both tell tales about magical acts and entertainments — and Odysseus even talks about a "ringmaster" who is also a singer and musician. The Greeks liked mimes, too — and when they held their famous athletic contests, they'd often have circus-like entertainments as part of the spectacle.

Some historians claim that the circus was a Roman invention, especially because they had the perfect places to hold three-ring events — like the Colosseum and the Circus Maximus. The Romans did give us the name "circus," but their early entertainments by that name included chariot races — which also had origins from the Greeks, Egyptians and Etruscans. Other writers said they thought there were probably circuses in every culture because folks just like to challenge the rules of nature. They want to try their hand at taming wild animals…walking on tiny wires…soaring through space on trapezes…and dressing up in outlandish get-ups. In some lands, it seems circus-type events were even part of religious life! That notion would be sure to get Father riled up, since his idea of "church" was to sit straight and quiet in a pew listening to the preacher talk in hushed tones!

It's amazing what people all over the world have done to amaze their friends and neighbors — whether just for fun, or as part of an organized circus-type event. Up in Alaska, there are Eskimos that do a sword-swallowing type routine, except what they swallow is a smooth stick about a foot-and-a-half long! Ouch! In India, people sit or lie on beds of stakes or nails. They also do incredible contortions — rolling themselves into all kinds of shapes while willing themselves into a trance! They claim to be able to charm snakes, too — making even large and dangerous snakes do their bidding.

Now, the Greller circus that came to Liberty Falls didn't include a fire-eater, but there have been folks who walked on fire and swallowed fire in lots of circuses all over the world — including India and Greece. And imagine this: in order to prove himself a man, every young South Pacific lad centuries ago had to put himself into a trance and jump from a tower with a piece of vine tied to his ankle. Just a few inches before he'd hit the ground, the vine would extend fully and pop him back up again — at least in most cases, I guess!

Another part of the circus that seems to have long-ago roots is the fact that circus folks travel around all the time. The books call that being "nomadic." The Greller circus goes from town to town all over the West from about April through October, then heads Down South to work on new acts, paint their wagons, and rest up for another season. The same was true in the past: in fact, the most successful animal trainers in Roman circuses were actually people who traveled there from Egypt!

Getting back to Greller's circus and what goes on here in America, our own country has quite a tradition of its own — with one of the most remarkable events taking place in 1793 in Philadelphia. That's when a Scotsman by the name of John Bill Ricketts set up what experts call the first full-fledged American circus — one with clowns, horses, music, and acrobatic acts all in one show. Ricketts himself amazed the crowd by juggling four oranges while riding his horse at full speed!

Elephants first joined American circuses in the early 1800s, although some religious fanatics seemed to think it was their duty to shoot circus elephants, calling their antics "sinful." Maybe Father would agree! Meanwhile, circuses became a regular feature at New York's Madison Square, in a tented building called the Hippodrome.

I'm sure you've all heard of P.T. Barnum, but I bet you haven't heard the name he gave to his show back in 1873: "P.T. Barnum's Great Traveling World's Fair, Consisting of Museum, Menagerie, Caravan, Hippodrome, Gallery of Statuary and Fine Arts, Polytechnic Institute, Zoological Garden, and 100,000 Curiosities, Combined with Dan Castello's, Sig Sebastian's, and Mr. D'Atlelie's Grand Triple Equestrian and Hippodromatic Exposition." The title alone is enough to tire folks out, before they even got to the show! Now —

and since 1888 — Barnum's been calling his circus "The Greatest Show on Earth." That's much easier to remember, I reckon!

When the railroad opened up the West, circuses were not far behind — eventually going into competition with circus-type "Wild West" shows like those of Buffalo Bill Cody. You know, he's been here in Liberty Falls many times, the old timers tell me — but that was before I was born. These days Buffalo Bill is so popular he only travels to big cities like Denver!

Anyway, that gives you an idea of what I found out, thanks to Miss Martin and Miss Adams and the library. After doing all this reading last winter, I had to put the circus in the back of my mind for awhile. After all, it would be months until summer! I bided my time and when warm weather rolled around, I was thrilled to see circus posters being put up all over Main Street! Eric and I counted down the days, keeping ourselves busy doing odd jobs for the neighbors so we'd have some extra spending money for cotton candy and souvenirs.

On the evening before the big circus parade, Eric's friend Joey came running up onto our front porch, breathless from running. "They're here, they're here! Come see!" he yelled. Father was out at a lodge meeting, and Mother looked up from her mending long enough to smile and nod "yes." "Be back by 8:30 or your father will have my head!" she warned. Then she softened and smiled. "Say hello to the elephants for me!" she chuckled.

Joey and Eric and I ran all the way to the Fairgrounds, which the circus would use for its headquarters. The place was abuzz with activity. The elephants were being bathed — their keepers used huge scrub brushes with six-foot handles just to reach the enormous creatures' backs. What a thrill to see (and even to smell!) an elephant in person after reading about them in books for so long. I got chills, I was so excited!

The lions and tigers were still in their wagons, pacing and baring their teeth. They couldn't come out, I gather, until secure rings could be set up for practice. That was perfectly all right with me! I didn't want to confront them, although the boys picked up imaginary whips and chairs and pretended to tame the wild beasts. The animal wagons were glorious! The tigers' vehicle was bright red with gold trim, and the lions' wagon was green and gold. One of the roustabouts told us that the red wagon would be hitched up to four matched white horses, and the green wagon had an elephant to pull it during the parade.

The Big Top tent was about half set-up when we got there. We could tell it was going to be spectacular: all red, white and blue with stripes and stars and golden flags. Off to the side, trying to stay out of the dust, were some of the circus performers limbering up for a rehearsal. The clowns didn't have costumes or make-up on, but we could tell they were jesters by their movements and expressions. The tightrope walkers and acrobats were easy to pick out as well — they were very nimble and light on their feet, and so graceful! After awhile, the ring-master himself came over for a chat. He was Peter Greller, brother of our own Mr. Greller, the pharmacist. "Good evening, young folks," he said pleasantly. "I'm afraid I'm going to have to ask you to leave now. We need to get all the people and animals settled down for the night. See you at the parade tomorrow afternoon?" We nodded and said "Yessirree! Wouldn't miss it for the world!"

That night I dreamed about the elephants, walking in a line…I smelled roasted peanuts and tasted sweet cotton candy in my mouth. The next day Eric and I did our chores willingly, as a way to pass the time until 1 p.m. when the parade would begin. By noon we were in place on the steps of City Hall, anticipating the big event. Mother even joined us, parasol in hand, to avoid freckling her skin in the mid-summer sun.

At a few minutes before 1:00, we heard the faraway sounds of calliope music. My heart leaped! Right on time, the parade made its way through town, to the cheers and applause of hundreds of Liberty Falls folks! Mr. Greller the ringmaster waved and winked at Eric and me as he came by. What a happy way to be recognized! The elephants were so dignified as they marched quietly through town. The horses — how elegant! They bobbed their heads and pranced so proudly, show-ing off the beautiful wagons they pulled. The clowns did tricks as they made their way down the street, and one even walked on his hands for awhile. Bringing up the rear were two clowns with a large sign that said "Greller's Family Circus Big Top, 7:00 p.m. tonight, Liberty Falls Fairgrounds."

That night the show was everything I could have imagined and more. I remember the smells as much as the sounds and sights. Roasted peanuts, sweet cotton candy, hay, and of course the natural odors of wild animals. I loved every minute! The music was so melodic and cheery...the costumes so colorful...the performances so daring! I caught a glimpse of Mother as she watched the tightrope walkers. She looked enchanted! Her face softened so in the gaslight glow that she looked almost like a little girl, enjoying the wonder of the moment.

For weeks after the circus performance I fantasized about running away to join the Grellers as a trapeze artist or tightrope walker. I was sure I could pick up the skills I needed under the watchful eye of Peter Greller and the rest of his circus cast. I imagined this all in such detail that when I let my secret plan slip that night at dinner, I had almost convinced myself that it could be real! That is, until Father threw cold water on my idea with his harsh response!

The day after Father's pronouncement that "no child of mine will ever join the circus," I visited Miss Martin at her home. I confessed my plans to her, and told her of my Father's reaction. "Now Adrienne, I can imagine how disappointed and frustrated you must be. But your father does have a point. Do you remember how I helped you find the library books about the circus? Let's go back to the library and see if we can find out something about the life of circus runaways. Then you can make an informed decision for yourself!"

I love Miss Martin! She never tries to tell me exactly what to do like Father does. Instead, she helps me find the books and articles that can help me make up my own mind. And thank heavens she did! With Miss Martin's help — and some guidance from Miss Adams the librarian — I found a personal account of the life of a young boy who had run away to join the circus. The work was hard, and even though he wanted to become a trapeze artist, the circus owners just laughed at him and told him to keep feeding and cleaning up after the animals. It seems that trapeze artist training was reserved for family members only! With no money and no connections, he had no way to get back home. Worst of all, in one town he fell asleep under a tree and missed the circus caravan when it left! He was reduced to begging until he was found by a kindly street minister who eventually helped him get a railroad ticket back home.

After reading that account, some of the romance of circus life was erased from my mind. But I still wanted to make something special of my life! Again, Miss Martin came to my rescue. "Adrienne, I'm taking the train to the University of Colorado next week for a seminar on Middle School curriculum development. Would you like to come along?" I readily agreed, and much to my amazement, Father did, too.

When we arrived in Boulder, I was awestruck by the beauty and size of the University of Colorado buildings. Even more exciting to me was the fact that there were many women students there — a point I gather Miss Martin had hoped I would notice. "Could I come here to study after high school, Miss Martin?" I asked after our day-long visit. "There's no reason why not, Adrienne," Miss Martin answered. "This is a state university, open to all of our citizens — men and women alike. And with the way you've taken to research in the library, I can almost guarantee you'll succeed at any course of study you might choose!"

The new school year is beginning now, and I have a new reason to study hard. Even Father has agreed that if my grades remain high, I can apply to the University of Colorado once I finish high school. I'm thinking of studying to be a teacher like Miss Martin — or maybe even a librarian like Miss Adams. When I talk about going to college, Mother gets that same glow of excitement and anticipation in her eyes that she did when she first heard about the circus! No matter how many times I visit a circus I know there'll always be a part of me that wants to fly from that trapeze. But now I have a new ambition — to learn, and to teach — and I have a feeling my students-to-be will fill my life with as much delight and fulfillment as any three-ring circus!

The calliope that came to Liberty Falls with the Greller Family Circus looked much like this one.

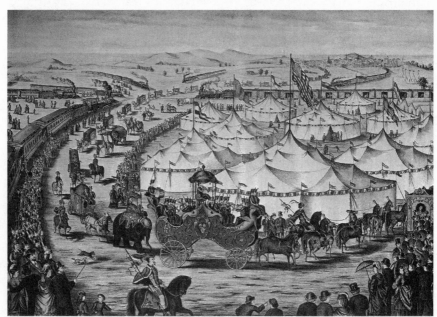

When the circus was all set up on the Liberty Falls Fairgrounds, it looked so exotic that Adrienne and her brother were overcome with excitement!

CHAPTER VII

Religious Life in the Old West

A colorful account of the diversity of faith in Liberty Falls... as told by one of our town's newer "men of the cloth" — Pastor George Kendell of the Church of the Epiphany

'm sure you've heard the phrase many times: "The Lord works in mysterious ways." And my wife Marjorie and I are here to attest to the wisdom of that statement! All through my early years in college and seminary, Marjorie and I subsisted in "cold water flats" with very little room and even less privacy. We imagined it would be pretty much the same when we got our first church assignment, assuming that it would be in a big city like New York or Philadelphia. But imagine our surprise when we were called to a brand-new church in Liberty Falls, Colorado — complete with a wonderful little cottage we can call our own! While this cozy house is surely one of the more modest structures in the thriving town of Liberty Falls, my wife and I consider it our ideal home.

Our local parishioners seem pleased as well with how we Kendells took to the parsonage they provided. Marjorie planted flowers and shrubs, and I built a gate with an arbor for climbing roses. We even added a bird bath to our yard, and placed a garden bench on the lawn so that we and our guests can enjoy the view. Recently, just a year after we arrived in Liberty Falls, we welcomed our first child — a boy we named Jeremiah. So I guess you could say we're truly the picture of "domestic tranquillity," Liberty Falls style!

When Marjorie and I set out for Liberty Falls from the East Coast by train, we had very little idea what to expect. Visions of dusty streets, cowboys, saloons and prospectors with mules ran through our heads. Much to our amazement, when we arrived in town we were ushered to a stunning new structure — the Church of the Epiphany — built by Liberty Falls residents according to plans drawn up by a noted Denver architect! Folks in town were rightly proud of the church's dramatic features — notably its double-staircase entrance, arched windows, and steeple complete with a bell and a shining, sculpted cross at the top. I was awestruck! I promised myself right then and there that the preaching and teaching that went on inside this glorious structure would befit its beauty and splendor. Yes, we offer much more than Sunday services. We also do our best to provide folks of all ages with week-long fellowship and educational experiences.

The Rev. Mr. Smith holds his congregation mesmerized with his latest "fire and brimstone" sermon.

Before church each week, adults gather in small groups to read passages from the Bible and discuss their applications in everyday life. Young people work on service projects, providing entertainment and diversion to shut-ins and delivering food baskets to the needy. The little ones have their own choir and drama group, and once a month or so they show off their accomplishments as part of the "grownups' service." Most delightful of all is our weekly Wednesday night supper. It's held outside on the church grounds in good weather, or in the church basement when it rains or gets too cold. Folks from other churches come too — anyone is more than welcome if they just bring their own eating utensils and a covered dish to pass!

Pastor George Kendell was delighted when he and his wife Marjorie were assigned to the handsome new Church of the Epiphany, complete with a "clergy cottage."

Over the course of a month or so, we often play host to visitors from more than a dozen houses of worship during those Wednesday night events. Yes, I can assure you that Liberty Falls comes honestly by its Colorado reputation as a "city of churches." Why, in these pioneer boom days it seems that very few years pass without the establishment of yet another God-fearing congregation. And thus the recent building of the Pioneer's Chapel was met with joy by the townsfolk, who would now have yet another choice for their worship and fellowship — and another pastor in town working for the betterment of all. Reverend Patrick Muir was the gentleman tapped to help build this new flock — and the congregation started off small but enthusiastic. The Reverend — a single gent — makes his home in the handsome little rectory cottage right next door to the sanctuary. When he arrived he was most pleased to see that the ladies of his parish already had planted climbing roses — and the men had seen to it that the church was surrounded by healthy young trees and shrubs. "This is God's house, and it's fitting that it be surrounded by His bountiful growing things," the Reverend commented one day when I visited him — spreading his hands to take in the beauty in his midst. Many an afternoon did I spy him reading his sacred books and enjoying the view from the bench on the church's front lawn!

Another new place of worship on the local scene is the handsome little Friend's Community Church. A proud and tall bell tower makes this church visible from blocks away — and on Sunday mornings, Preacher Smith himself rings the bell to call his "flock" from far and wide. The church looks conservative and conventional from the outside — what with its elegant windows, and the trees and bushes that nestle snugly against its foundation. But The Reverend Mr. Smith soon gained a reputation here in town as quite the spirited preacher! So much so that on one of my rare Sundays off, I slipped into a back pew of his church to see what all the excitement was about. Oh, he begins his sermons calmly enough, but after he gets warmed up, watch out! He'll preach fire and brimstone for an hour straight. And his message is so compelling that you can't hear a pin drop! Rumor has it that even Snake Eye Jake stops in from time to time to hear "Old Rev. Smith" shake the rafters. Jake told me he considers it "downright great entertainment." Far be it from that old scoundrel to admit his need for Christian redemption! To the faithful, though, Preacher Smith's weekly sermon provides a Sunday's worth of spiritual inspiration at its finest.

As our town of Liberty Falls grows and prospers, every religious sect seems intent on building a church to reflect its particular views and methods of worship. Some churches hold Sunday services with a strict one-hour time limit, while others allow their preachers to go "on and on" until well after most folks' preferred time for the midday meal! Some church parishes enjoyed a great deal of singing, with hymn after hymn ringing out over the landscape. Other groups seem perfectly satisfied with one hymn at the beginning of the service and another at the close. They don't even care if the choir shows up for an anthem!

St. Paul's United Church has found its own special niche as the home for those of Scandinavian heritage. Not only do they enjoy religious fellowship here, but also a place where their traditions of culture, holidays, music, dance and costume can be continued with vibrancy and beauty. Indeed, the church now is known throughout Colorado for its annual Scandinavian Festival, which draws visitors not only from Liberty Falls, but from throughout the West as well. And the church's minister, The Reverend Henry Swenson, does all he can to bring the religious and social traditions of Sweden, Norway and Finland to life for his "flock" in Liberty Falls.

As you can see from just these few examples, Liberty Falls is a veritable melting pot of cultures and heritages. But when it comes to religion, most folks in these parts resist that "melting" part. They don't want to assimilate so much that they lose their faith and its rituals. As one of my parishioners told me, "I prefer to think about America as a crazy quilt or tapestry — all jumbled together but with the individual pieces and colors still visible and separate enough to view and appreciate." I reckon that's why we boast so many places of worship here in town. Why, I haven't even mentioned Father O'Flaherty of the Catholic church, nor Rabbi Lewis of the Jewish synagogue. There are even some citizens in town who practice Eastern religions: Chinese folk particularly, who migrated this way after their parents came to America during the California Gold Rush!

Many of these diverse congregations began meeting in school rooms or even in each others' homes — but considering the wealth in this town due to mining, it wasn't long before most of them were able to raise the money necessary to build and furnish their own places of worship. In fact, many of the richest men and women in Colorado were instrumental in funding our state's elegant churches. They consider it a way to make a visible statement of thanks for their good fortune — one that will remain long after they are gone!

I've been impressed with the level of tolerance and appreciation

Liberty Falls citizens show for each others' religious traditions. But that's as it should be, since so many of the immigrants to this land came here in the first place to escape religious tyranny! I've been preparing a series of sermons on this very theme — and if you'd like I can share a few of the highlights of what I've learned about the fascinating religious history of the American people!

Starting at the very beginning, perhaps you've heard about how Leif Ericson arrived in North America by mistake many hundreds of years ago. His trip was probably the first religious foray into the New World, since he was supposedly on his way to Greenland to spread Christianity for King Olaf Tryggvason of Norway! Christopher Columbus was on a religious mission as well, and as you know he landed on Thursday, October 11, 1492 at an island he named San Salvador (which means Holy Savior). Columbus said of the people there, "I believe that they would easily be made Christian, as it appeared to me they had no religion."

Of course, many other voyagers to the New World had religious motives. Some came to this land to bring their faith to others, while others fled persecution based on their beliefs. While some of the colonies set themselves apart as havens for certain religions, Rhode Island served as perhaps the best "role model" for what we see here today in Liberty Falls. Not only did Rhode Island welcome Baptists, Quakers, Anglicans (later Episcopalians) and Congregationalists, but it also became a significant colonial center for Catholicism and Judaism.

Recently I asked Rabbi Lewis if I could borrow some of his books about Jewish history. And what I learned was fascinating! Back in those colonial days, there were less than a dozen active Jewish congregations in the New World — but during this last century the number of Jews in America has multiplied over and over again. This is not to minimize Jewish contributions to Early American life. At least two Jews sailed with Columbus, and one scholar I read argued that Columbus himself might well have been Jewish. History books tell us, though, that the main Jewish religious history in the United States began with the arrival of Portuguese-speaking refugees from Recife in Eastern Brazil in the mid-1600s. They landed at New

Amsterdam, and established Congregation Shearith Israel (Remnant of Israel) about 20 years later. Several other Jewish congregations were incorporated during the 1700s — notably in Newport, New Haven, Charleston, Savannah, Richmond and Philadelphia.

The largest increase in Jewish immigration came when German Jews fled anti-Semitic laws and other oppressive conditions to come to America. It is estimated that in 1840 there were 15,000 Jews in the United States, which grew to 50,000 in 1850, to 160,000 in 1860, and finally to 250,000 in 1880. Another estimate states that 200,000 Jews immigrated to the United States during the course of the 19th century.

Most of those Jewish folk are still clustered in the larger cities Back East. When they arrived they found their quickest way to make a living was in the retail trades. Many started very humbly, as peddlers of suspenders or "Yankee notions," which the Jews called Kuttle Muttle. Working hard and taking advantage of every opportunity, Jewish Americans soon advanced into considerable success, as a recent federal survey reveals. Here are some facts about the Jewish population in 1890:

- Less than 2% are laborers or peddlers
- Almost half are in business
- 30% are in clerical or sales positions
- 5% are in the professions
- 40% employ at least one servant
- 20% employ two servants
- 10% employ three servants or more

Another group that finds great strength in its religious roots is that of the freed slaves. Particularly since Emancipation, the church has become second only to the family as the most important institution in life for black people. These folks relate to their church all week long — not just on Sundays. The church provides a method for economic cooperation, a social network, and a refuge from continuing discrimination. Now at the turn of the century, 90% of freed slaves still live in the South, but here in Colorado we do have a significant black population. While the black churches in Denver are far more prominent than in the smaller cities and towns, we do have a thriving African Methodist Episcopal congregation here in Liberty Falls.

My studies of the Revivalists have also proven of great interest — particularly the biography of Dwight Lyman Moody, who died just recently in 1899. Born in Massachusetts, young Moody became a Boston shoe salesman when he was still a teenager. He became a church member in 1856 at the age of 19, and moved to Chicago that same year. Moody found himself on fire with the Holy Spirit, and he soon rented four pews in Chicago's Plymouth Congregational Church to fill with street people and down-and-out folks from the local boarding houses. By 1863 he had formed his own Illinois Street Church, and gained support of wealthy industrialists including George Armour and Cyrus McCormick.

In addition to his church work, Moody became the driving force behind Chicago's YMCA (Young Men's Christian Association). But by the 1870s it was clear that his true calling was in saving folks from their sins. Why, in one sermon that took place in London, England in 1872, Moody single-handedly called 400 people to his closing invitation to accept the Lord! His message was simple but compelling. He'd stand in front of his audience and hold his Bible aloft. In comforting and reassuring tones, he'd assert that eternal life was theirs for the taking. All they had to do was, in his words, "Come forward and t-a-k-e, TAKE!" Once people responded to the altar call, he'd implore them to "Join some church at once." Frankly, the last time I heard our own Reverend Smith preach, I thought I was seeing a reincarnation of Moody himself, right here in Colorado!

But back to my point about Rhode Island. In Liberty Falls we have what I believe to be as harmonious an atmosphere of religious tolerance as you're likely to find most anywhere. Protestants, Catholics and Jews serve together in city government, and you'll see both a decorated evergreen and a handsome menorah adorning our Town Square in December. Even the various Protestant sects "agree to disagree" on the finer points of their faith — they remember well that it's only been a few short years since they all worshiped together in a tent when Liberty Falls was a humble mining camp.

Now, I'm not saying that Liberty Falls is "heaven on earth." We have a horrific fight going on these days about prohibition, with our religious leaders and congregations sharply divided on whether it should be illegal to sell alcohol. There are almost as many saloons and dance halls in town as there are churches, and our sheriff keeps plenty busy breaking up fights and catching perpetrators of all manner of misdeeds in these parts. But for Marjorie and me, this assignment has been a Godsend. Fresh air and gorgeous mountains, an active and positive congregation, a growing town, a beautiful church — and this cozy little cottage all our own. Here's hoping the Kendells are called to stay here in Liberty Falls for many years to come!

A SHORT LIST OF LIBERTY FALLS RELIGIONS
By Pastor George Kendell

I may be leaving a few sects out, but here are the religions I've counted to date in and around Liberty Falls:

African Methodist Episcopal
Baptist
Congregational
Episcopal
Jewish
Lutheran (Finnish, German and Swedish)
Mennonite
Methodist
Presbyterian
Puritan
Quaker
Reformed (Dutch, French and German)
Roman Catholic
Unitarian
Various Eastern Religions

CHAPTER VIII

Onward, Temperance Soldiers!...
The Saloon Must Go

A rousing declaration of war against "demon rum" and the rogues that sell it to local citizens...as told by the leader of the Liberty Falls Ladies Temperance Society, Harriet Shaw

ercy me! Liberty Falls is still quite the wild and woolly place compared to my hometown of Churchville, New York. But thanks to the upstanding Christian women of our local Liberty Falls Ladies Temperance Society, I stand firm in the belief that we will rid this community of the "devil's brew" in very short order! Oh, I had my doubts when I first moved here with my late husband Clarence — why, it seemed as if characters like that unsavory Snake Eye Jake practically ran this town back then! But year by year, Liberty Falls

Chanting "The Saloon Must Go," Mrs. Shaw and some of her fellow temperance advocates take matters into their own hands outside one of Liberty Falls' notorious "watering holes."

advances in all the civilized arts and cultures — not to mention the fact that churches now outnumber saloons in our fair city! Praise God!

Come on in and sit a spell with me. I love to have folks join me here at the Temperance Society house. Did you know it was a gift from Mrs. Nellie Clemenson, who passed away a few years back? Oh, yes — she was one of our charter members along with Mrs. Tully of the General Store, Abigail Martin the school principal, and several other of our more refined female citizens. I'll tell you, there was quite a stir when Mrs. Clemenson's will was read. You see, the Town Fathers thought that Nellie has written up her will leaving this big, beautiful house to the City. Heaven knows what the menfolk would have done with it, but we ladies knew exactly how we could use the home in a way that would have made Nellie proud.

After we're done chatting, take a look around! You'll see that we've done a fine job keeping up Nellie's garden, and all the ladies have contributed furnishings so that our regular meetings are comfortable and cozy. Upstairs you'll find several bedrooms which we rent to young, single women who are new in town — schoolteachers and the like. Miss Martin says that the availability of a safe, "ladies-only" accommodation has made her job of recruiting new schoolmarms ever so much easier the last few years!

My fellow members of the Temperance Society and I are planning to try and make Colorado a dry state, and we think we have a pretty good chance of success now that women have the opportunity to vote in these parts. That's right, we're pretty proud that Colorado was the second state to allow for women's suffrage, starting in 1893! Before moving statewide, however, we'll be taking a local course of action to try to outlaw drinking in these parts. I've already started talking with Mayor Willie Griffin to see if we can win him over to our point of view, but I have to admit, it may well be a difficult task. Why, I've noticed the Mayor hob-nobbing time and again with that Mr. Ausberg of the brewery — and Mrs. Tully told me she spied the Mayor stopping in at that new tavern on Main Street: and it wasn't just to welcome the owner to the neighborhood!

Not that I'm as opposed to beer and wine as I am to hard liquor. Indeed, back before distilled spirits became commonplace throughout Europe during the 1700s, drunkenness was hardly ever a big problem! Sad but true though, with today's excessive drinking on the part of many menfolk, we ladies have concluded that the only way to save the American family is for every right-thinking gent to "take the pledge" and swear off drinking entirely! How can you blame us, considering that a town like Cripple Creek, Colorado is known to have over 57 saloons, in operation 24 hours a day — as opposed to just 14 churches! And I don't even want to speculate on what's going on at the Cripple Creek establishment they call "The Wayfarer's Inn"! I've heard gents call it a "sporting house," but gambling isn't the only devilish attraction, I'm afraid, considering all the fancy-dressed women that inhabit the place!

If you know anything about history, you may have run across the accounts of attempts to control folks' "overindulgence" as far back as the ancient civilizations. That's right — stop by our local Library and Reading Room if you don't believe me! China, Palestine, Egypt, India and Greece are just a few of the countries with "drinking problems" in their histories. But it wasn't until this century that excessive drinking became such a horrendous social enemy that we ladies (and some gents as well) felt compelled to establish Temperance Societies throughout Europe and the United States.

The first temperance group I've heard about was the one in Skibbereen, Ireland, which started back in 1818. Then in 1829, the Ulster Temperance Society was formed, and soon after that groups in Scotland and England gained strength. In the United States, churches have established a core of support for the Temperance Movement, and the same took place in England, where the Church of England Temperance Society was chartered in 1862.

Cleveland, Ohio was the original home of the Woman's Christian Temperance Union (WCTU), which began in 1847. Then by the 1870s, a veritable "temperance crusade" was sweeping across the United States, thanks in great measure to a woman I admire above all others. Frances Willard was her name, and she was a contemporary of my mother's back in Churchville, New York. Mrs. Willard died recently, but before she did she made quite a mark for herself — both as a temperance advocate and as an educator.

As my mother told me so many times, Frances Elizabeth Caroline Willard was an ambitious and bright girl — perhaps the smartest of her generation in all of Churchville. Frances was just 17 when she traveled halfway across the country to attend the Milwaukee Female College. The next year she entered Northwestern Female College in Evanston, Illinois, and graduated just two years later as valedictorian! Then all the while she was teaching and later presiding over the Evanston College for Ladies, Frances was a stalwart of the Temperance Movement. Indeed, she became president of the Chicago chapter of the Woman's Christian Temperance Union — and then president of the national organization! Eventually she even presided over the worldwide WCTU — the first person ever to do so.

Another woman I admire quite a lot is Susan B. Anthony. She's been active both in the Temperance Movement, and in helping gain women the right to vote. Indeed, she founded her National Woman Suffrage Association way back in 1869. Susan stirred up quite a ruckus when she insisted on voting in the presidential election of 1872, just to test her "status as a citizen," as she put it. The menfolk put her on trial, and fined her $100. I thought Susan had a great rebuttal for them: the best since the Boston Tea Party! She refused to pay, stating that "taxation without representation is tyranny!"

You know, even when Frances Willard and my mother were girls, the Temperance Movement was getting started in various parts of the United States and its territories. Back before the Civil War, what they call "religious revivalism" took hold all across the land, and controlling liquor was a major part of what the revivalists called for. At first they asked only for "moderation," but before long they were calling for "abstinence," just as we do here in Liberty Falls at the Temperance Society.

Speaking of the Civil War, I wonder if you're aware that President Abraham Lincoln himself was a long-time supporter of the Temperance Movement. Why, our leaders still hand down tales about Lincoln's fiery speech back in the late 1830s at the South Fork School

House in Sangamon County, Illinois. Farmers and other folk from those parts came to listen to Lincoln speak and to "sign the pledge." Even children were encouraged to sign: the earlier the better to help nurture a life-long plan of abstinence. A 10-year-old boy named Cleopas Breckenridge signed, and Lincoln himself told the lad, "Now, Sonny keep that pledge and it will be the best act of your life." Boys who signed were called "Lincolns," and girls were called "Willards" after my mother's old friend Frances Willard.

Whether you were for the North or the South in the War Between the States, you'd have a "dry" hero to look up to, for General Robert E. Lee himself was a temperate man. As Lee wrote in 1869, "My experience through life has convinced me that while moderation and temperance in all things are commendable and beneficial, abstinence from spirituous liquors is the best safeguard to morals and health." Praise be, General Lee!

In case you want to take it yourself, here is the wording for "the pledge" — the same pledge we encourage folks to sign here in Liberty Falls even today:

The Pledge

Whereas, the use of intoxicating liquors as a beverage is productive of pauperism, degradation and crime; and believing it our duty to discourage that which produces more evil than good, we therefore pledge ourselves to abstain from the use of intoxicating liquors as a beverage.

Now, if you'd like to take the pledge right away, just let me know and I'll prepare one of our certificates for you. It has "the pledge" in beautiful script along with a place for you to sign and put your address and date. You could even frame it and put it on the wall if you've a mind to! But I'm getting off track. Back to my story.

Right after the Civil War, a new political party became part of the Temperance Movement. It was called the Prohibition Party, and its goal was the complete abolition of "liquor traffic." The party formed officially on September 1, 1869, when about 500 delegates — men and women alike — convened in Chicago's Farwell Hall. While another organization called the Anti-Saloon League believed in convincing regular party candidates to embrace prohibition, the Prohibition Party proposed its own presidential candidates. We might just try that in Liberty Falls — it could be wise to get someone to run against Mayor Griffin if he continues consorting in taverns and saloons!

Now you know, listening to me rant and rave about the menfolk, you might think I believe it's all their fault that they fall prey to Demon Rum. But nothing could be further from the truth. Women bear much of the responsibility of ensuring a happy and harmonious family life — and if the lady of the house does not do her duty, sadly the man may well be lured away by the charms of the streets. As Mrs. Cornelius wrote in "The Young Housekeeper's Friend," a booklet my mother gave me before my marriage to Clarence:

How often do we see the happiness of a husband abridged by the absence of skill, neatness and economy in the wife! Perhaps he is not able to fix upon the cause, for he does not understand minutely enough the processes upon which domestic order depends, to analyze the difficulty; but he is conscious of discomfort. However improbable it may seem, the health of many a professional man is undermined, and his usefulness curtailed, if not sacrificed, because he habitually eats bad bread.

There are numerous instances of worthy merchants and mechanics, whose efforts are paralyzed, and their hopes chilled by the total failure of the wife in her sphere of duty; and who seek solace under their disappointment in the wine-party, or the late convivial supper. Many a day-laborer, on his return at evening from his hard toil, is repelled by the sight of a disorderly house, and a comfortless supper; and perhaps is met by a cold eye instead of "the thriftie wifie's smile;" and he makes his escape to the grog-shop, or the underground gambling room.

So ladies, beware! Just as the husband's duty is to remain sober and temperate, the wife's job is to keep a neat and comfortable home and put a good supper on the table at a regular time each evening! Indeed, according to what I've been reading lately from the Anti-Saloon

League, many of my fellow advocates now believe education about domestic duties and the deleterious effects of alcohol may well be the best effort we in the Temperance Movement may undertake.

The Anti-Saloon League is one of the newer temperance organizations, and unlike our Ladies Temperance Society here in Liberty Falls, it includes both men and women as members. The group's motto is, "The Saloon Must Go," and they use local churches to help carry their message and solicit funds. Before long there will be an Anti-Saloon League in just about every state in the nation, and millions of our citizenry will hear the League's vital message through the printed word. Why, our local printer Mr. Cummings has already printed several thousand leaflets for the local League, and as well as a number of stories aimed at helping spread our message to adults and children alike.

One of my favorite "temperance tales" is called "Esther's First Party," and if reading that story wouldn't get a man to take the pledge — I don't know what would! It tells the saga of a little girl named Esther who is saddened and embarrassed by her father's plunge into the bottle. Esther asks her mother what can be done to convince her father to take "the pledge," and the mother suggests that Esther try to intervene. How could the father resist when the little girl told him, "God will help if you do your part. If you sign the pledge you will not want to break your promise and that will help you keep it."

The father signed the pledge and Esther and her mother immediately planned a gala party to celebrate. This was "Esther's First Party," because heretofore she could never count on her father to make a sober appearance when her friends were visiting. Everyone had a wonderful time at the party, not the least of whom was Esther's father — so overjoyed was he with the transformation of his daughter into a happy and carefree child! That night, after Esther was asleep, her father tiptoed into her room and kissed her on the forehead. He knelt beside her bed and renewed his vow never to drink again. Then he prayed to God for the strength he would need to carry out his pledge! Aah, perhaps I should tell that story this Sunday during the Children's Moments at church. If the fathers are listening, I would imagine I could gather quite a few pledges in the social hour after the services, do you agree?

Speaking of the churches, our Temperance Society has enjoyed excellent cooperation from many of the clergymen hereabouts. In fact, most all of the churches in town have adopted this stirring anthem as part of their regular hymn singing:

Onward, Temperance Soldiers!
By James Rowe and Arthur Sullivan
(to the tune of "Onward Christian Soldiers")

On-ward, temp'rance sol-diers, bravely on-ward go;
We must free our country from this aw-ful foe;
Let there be no quar-ter given, but, with joy,
This destroying de-mon utterly destroy.

On-ward temperance soldiers, to the holy war;
Jesus Christ your Captain, trod the way before.

On-ward, temp'rance sol-diers, children starve and die,
Mothers, loving mothers, bruis'd and bleeding lie;
"Double quick" the or-der, Onward, then, with speed;
Souls in sor-row call us, souls despair-ing plead.

On-ward temperance soldiers, to the holy war;
Jesus Christ your Captain, trod the way before.

On-ward, temp'rance sol-diers; true and fearless be,
Till our deal Col-um-bia from this curse is free,
Surely God will shield us, and no harm shall come;
We must free our country from this monster Rum.

On-ward temperance soldiers, to the holy war;
Jesus Christ your Captain, trod the way before.

In addition to the churches, we have Miss Abigail Martin on our side. She originally came to Liberty Falls as our first local schoolteacher, but now she is the principal of the Clemen's School as well. Miss Martin has published several handbills explaining the ill effects of liquor, which she shares with her students and their parents alike. Some of her diagrams and charts come from the WCTU, and others from the

Scientific Temperance Federation. As Cora Stoddard, who wrote the famous temperance pamphlet "Education on Wheels" said, "You can reach by this method (pamphlets and charts) thousands of people whom you cannot reach in any other way. But it must be teaching, not preaching." When people find out that everything from their equilibrium to their ability to add columns of numbers is adversely affected by alcohol, they usually sit up and take notice right quick.

Now you've been so nice to listen to all my stories, I feel I can make a little confession to you. Shocking as it seems, even though I myself took "the pledge" at the age of nine back in my hometown of Churchville, the sad fact is that alcohol has passed my lips once or twice. But not by my own design! Oh, no — I was the victim of a traveling salesman! Here's how it happened.

One early spring I was feeling a might poorly. It wasn't too long after my Clarence passed on, and I found myself in low spirits day after day. Then one afternoon I was walking along Main Street right here in Liberty Falls when I spied a gent selling "spring tonic" out of the back of his wagon. He told me it would cure my sickness and my sadness all at once. Sounded mighty persuasive, he did. So I bought a bottle. I took it home, poured myself a spoonful, and drank it down. It tasted quite strong, but low and behold, within a few minutes' time I started feeling better! Even had a pleasant tingling feeling in my limbs! "It's a miracle!" I cried. And I had a couple of more spoonsful.

About then, Miss Martin stopped by my home to see how I was doing. She'd been so kind during my mourning over Clarence. I must have looked a bit disorderly to her — she said my hair was in disarray and my glasses were a bit askew! She came in and asked me what I'd been up to, and I showed her the spring tonic. "Try it yourself, Abigail!" I urged her. But Miss Martin looked at the fine print on the back of the bottle and said in a stunned voice, "Harriet! This tonic is 30% alcohol! For shame!" I soon convinced Miss Martin that I had no idea what the tonic contained, and right there in her presence I poured the remaining tonic down my kitchen sink. We agreed to keep this unfortunate episode between the two of us, and I've never had spring tonic again. You won't tell anyone my secret, will you? I'm sure not.

Well, I'd love to keep chatting with you, but I need to stroll on home now to feed my cat, Prudence, and light the fire for supper. Feel free to wander through the house if you'd like — we love to show off the fine headquarters Nellie Clemenson left us. And don't forget, whenever you're ready to take "the pledge," just let me know. Remember…The Saloon Must Go! Bye, now.

Harriet Shaw had this poster framed as a decoration for the Liberty Falls Ladies Temperance Society meeting room.

CHAPTER IX

The Story of Trapper Big Mike

How rough and ready men earned a living in the Wild West trapping animals for furs and skins...as told by the last remaining fur trapper in Liberty Falls, Big Mike

Pull up a stool, friend — come here and join me! Can I buy you a beer or a sarsaparilla? I've had a mighty good month I have, true to tell! Just sold me a passel of furs and pelts, made enough money to stock up with everything I need for the next month up in my cabin in the woods. That's right, I purt-neer bought out Tully's General Store this afternoon! My donkey Bessie will be complainin' a sight when I load 'er up for the trip back home. Right now she's restin' out there in the shade with a bucket o' water and some of her favorite feed I

Trapper Big Mike and his donkey Bessie worked just as hard as this old-time trapper and his horse.

picked up for her at Swanson's Feed and Grain. So I'm takin' a rest here myself. That's right, the Gold Nugget Tavern is one of my reg'lar monthly stops — even if it's been a slow month and all I can afford is a quick shot of whiskey. I can't resist stoppin' in here for a game of faro with that varmint Snake Eye Jake. He and I have been friends since the Gold Rush! But from what I hear, Jake's tamed down quite a lot from his heyday. Yep, he's buildin' himself a little farmhouse on the outskirts of town and he spends most of his time there these days!

Ya know, lots of folks ask me if I'll ever give up the fur trade — after all, those modern thinkers b'lieve the era of profitable trappin' pretty much died out by the 1870s — and here it is 20 years later or so! But my idea is this: most of them other trappers are either dead and gone, or they've found themselves another line of business. So I have trappin' pretty much to myself in this part of Colorado! And I like the life I lead up there in the woods — even though Bessie the burro is 'bout the only one I have to talk to most days of the year! So as long as I can keep bringin' enough furs and skins into town each month to keep me fed and entertained, this'll be the life for me!

Have ya ever seen yourself a trapper's cabin? Oh, it's a purty sight if you like livin' in the woods like I do! When I first built my cabin it wasn't much more'n a lean-to. But come to think about it, I've been livin' there a good 30 years now. And in the spring and summertime when the trappin' is slow, I can spend my time fixin' up the cabin, growin' myself some food, practicin' my fiddle, cleanin' my guns and traps, and readin' the books I pick up every month at the Liberty Falls Library and Readin' Room! You've never seen anything so comely as my woods in full bloom with wildflowers in the spring. I try to look forward to that in the winter when the wind is howlin' and I have to put my snowshoes on jest to go outside and git some more wood for the fire! But now that I've got real glass windows with heavy quilted curtains, and a big old bed with one of "Aunt Alice" Willoughby's quilts on it, life is a good sight easier 'n it used to be.

Yep, I have it pretty posh these days, but I remember full well what it was like when I first arrived here in Colorado back around 1860. And anything I didn't know about the "ole days" I learned right quick by talkin' with the trappers who'd been around a spell. Lots of adventurous types headed out West to trap at the beginning of the century. Why? Because a passel of hoity-toity Englishmen decided they wanted fancy beaver hats to wear while strollin' by the Thames! That was enough to get the trappin' fever goin'. But the white men soon realized when they got here that the Indians wouldn't exactly cotton to them trappin' beaver just for the pelts. No sir-ree Bob! If you know anything 'bout Indian culture, I'm sure you're aware that they believe that animals should be treated with respect. If ya have to kill an animal, the Indians say, ya owe it to the animal and to nature itself to use every last speck of that critter — for clothing, for food, or whatever good use you could come up with!

Well, event'ally some of the Indians joined in with the white men in the trappin' business. They came to an agreement 'bout how their work would be done, what their division of labor would be and so on. I read a book about it once called *A Holiday With Fur Traders*. It was writ in 1839 by a young whippersnapper named Elias Willard Smith who was visitin' with the trappers and Indians. Smith described the Arapaho Indians and the "passin' of the peace pipe" like this:

They were all fine looking fellows, rather lighter-colored than our eastern Indians. Two or three squaws accompanied them — also pretty good looking. The chiefs seated themselves around the fire, forming a ring with Mr. Vasquez and commenced smoking their long pipes, which they passed around several times…Among their number was one Shian (Cheyenne) and one Blackfoot."

Speakin' of the squaws, some of the white trappers did end up marryin' Indian women — or at least claimin' them as their wives. And I havta confess I was pretty ashamed of many of the white men when I saw how hard they expected their women folk to work! Why, if I'd been lucky enough to have a helpmate like that I woulda been proud to labor side-by-side with her. But a lot of these fellers would empty their traps and then expect their squaws to do all the cleanin', dryin', sortin' and packin' the pelts! I'll tell ya about how I do my work in a minute or so — but talkin' about the Indians reminds me of some of the readin' I've been doing — thanks to the help of Miss Constance Adams over at the Library and Readin' Room!

Ya know, one of the greatest blessin's to me has been the fact that I stayed in school long enough to learn to read, write and cipher. Lots of the trappers couldn't read a word and they could hardly add — it was easy for unscrupulous types to take advantage of them when they sold their pelts. And they couldn't use readin' as an escape from the hum-drum of an existence all alone in the woods — which is what I do! Anyway, back to my point. One day I was tellin' Miss Adams how upset I was about how white men sometimes treat Indians. She told me she thought I'd want to know about the struggles of the freed slaves — so she got together some books for me to read.

After the slaves was freed by Lincoln in 1865, you know, many of 'em had little idea what to do for a livin', and discrimination was pretty strong. So a passel of former slaves, both male and female, headed out West. They found that even though they couldn't vote in the West, and their young'uns weren't often welcome in school, they could get jobs if they were willin' to work hard. Yep, many black men became railroad laborers, scouts, cowboys and trappers!

The story of one particular former slave woman, "Aunt" Clara Brown, made a big impression on me, too. It seems in the 1860s — right about the time I came West myself — "Aunt" Clara showed up in Central City, Colorado. She had lived a sad life. When she was young, she was separated from her husband and children in a slave auction! When she got to Central City, she worked as a laundress and even as a miner! Her original idea was to use her earnin's to help find her family, but that didn't work out. So instead, she decided to stake other black folks to get started in Colorado. They called her the "Angel of the Rockies," and it's a moniker that suits her! Later on, "Aunt" Clara did reunite with one of her daughters, but she never saw the rest of her family again!

There were already quite a few black folk in Denver in the 1860s — in fact, Miss Adams showed me a picture of the Zion Baptist Church at 20th and Arapahoe that was started way back in 1865! There were a couple 'a newspapers published by blacks in Denver too, including the famous "Colorado Statesman" and "Denver Star." Campbell AME Church started in 1886 in Denver, and Central Baptist Church, at 24th and California, opened its doors in 1891. Why, when Miss Adams got herself a copy of the 1890 census for the library (sent specially from Denver since she used to be a librarian there) she showed me that there were already 3,045 black citizens in that fair city!

Now not every former slave headed to the city, though. Did you ever hear tell about all the black and Mexican cowboys out on the range? Why, nearly a third of all the cowboys in the "Wild West" were black! For one thing, it seems the folks with darker skin (and maybe a taste of what it was like to deal with the uppity white men) got along better with the Indians — you hear about very few skirmishes between Indians and blacks and Mexicans. For another, rumor has it that the blacks had the very best of all the cowboy songs. And again, bein' a cowboy is hard work. For folks with little education and a need to survive, the trade at least gave you a fightin' chance!

One of the most famous black cowboys is Nat Love, better known as "Deadwood Dick." Born a slave in Tennessee he was, back in 1854. He actually wrote a book about himself, which Miss Adams lent me. What a survivor! As "Deadwood Dick" said, "Horses were shot out from under me, men killed around me, but always I escaped with a trifling wound at best." Good for him!

There were also plenty 'o black miners and even some black-owned mines in Colorado. For instance, in 1883, a group of black Denver businessmen founded the "Golden Chest Mining, Milling and Tunnel Co., and Peter Joseph and the Russell Brothers, all black, started Iron Duke Mining in the 1880s. One of the first gold discoveries in Idaho Springs was made by another black mine owner, Henry Parker. You can bet there's more than one black millionaire in Denver, I reckon! Even so, there were many blacks doing jobs like mine too — in the fur trade they were everything from servants, pack-horsemen, cooks and hunters to scouts and guides.

Some folks don't realize how many blacks have homesteaded in Colorado and surroundin' areas. But with the famous Homestead Act of 1862, anybody who farmed a piece of land for five years could claim it as his own. So even though the promise of "40 acres and a mule" to freed slaves didn't come through in the Old South, blacks who came West often picked up many more acres than that — thanks to the sweat of their brows! Some blacks even became cattle ranchers like Eugene Swanson of Agate, Colorado. His wife Cleo was the first postmistress in Agate, accordin' to what I hear.

Now I told you I'd explain a bit about how I do my work, didn't I? Since ya probably don't want to hike up into the woods with me to see my cabin, I'll describe it to ya, and tell a bit about trappin' and such! If ya ever have any designs on bein' a trapper yourself, better listen close! It's a dangerous line o' work. Why, legend says that one in four trappers dies on the job — froze to death, scalped, attacked by wild animals, lost, or any number of other bad ends! Lucky for me, after 30 years in the trade I'm still alive and kickin', so I must know at least a mite about what I'm doin'!

So now down to business. The main area of my cabin has one big room that contains a small table for eatin', a bigger one for workin' and my bed with the handsome new quilt on it. I use all the space I've got — I keep my ropes, snowshoes and traps hanging' down from the walls and ceilin's. I decorate the cabin with animal horns and teeth and such, and you'll always find my jug of home-made whiskey over in the corner!

Like I said before, in the old days the English wanted mostly beaver, but I'll trap just about any animal that can bring me a decent price for the skins. Trappin' season is winter time, for any number of reasons which I'm sure you can figger out. Firstly, in the winter the animals' furs are thicker and purtier. In the summer time a lot of these critters lose weight and their coats thin out for the hot weather! Nextly, in the winter we can follow a critter's tracks in the snow. No way to do that in the summer now, is there? Then again, in the winter food is harder to find for most critters, so they're more likely to snoop around in my traps lookin' for a treat. And finally — and this is important, too — when it's cold the animals won't start decomposin' before I pick 'em up from the traps. You can only trap beavers at the end of the winter, though. They hole up in their little houses called "lodges" when it's really cold, and they get stuck in there because the ponds the lodges empty onto get frozen. So when the ponds unfreeze in the spring, you'll find me down there ready to pick up some winter-drowsy beavers if I can!

It's pretty nippy for us trappers in the winter, though — so we usually wear a full face of whiskers to help keep us warm during the blizzards. The Indians taught us how to dress for cold weather with leggins instead of full pants, and loincloths underneath. We can take off the leggins real quick-like if we need to run fast, or to wade into the water for a wash-up. But they're nice and warm when the wind whips through the mountains! Another "must" for a trapper in winter is a good pair of snowshoes. Why, some 'o these Colorado mountain peaks get as much as 300" deep in snow. If you tried to walk on that snow with reg'lar shoes or boots you'd sink right down like quick sand. But the snowshoes even your weight out so you can walk on top of the snow.

Here's a tip you need to keep in mind when you're out in the woods and the critters are near. Always walk into the wind — never in the same direction of the wind. When you walk into the wind, it will carry your human scent away and the critters will be less likely to smell you. That way they'll be much more apt to check out your trap once you've gone away. Oh, by the way, we set the traps at dusk and check 'em at dawn. Jest so's you know.

Once I've emptied the traps, I skin the animals, then stretch the skins over a willow hoop for two or three days to dry. Next I've gotta scrape the skins, and stamp 'em with my trader's mark. Once I've got enough, I'll fold a passel of skins nice and square and tie 'em up in bundles of either 10 or 20 skins. Like I said before, some of them trappers with squaws would sit and smoke a pipe while she did all this work! But unless I can get Bessie the burro to help me, in my cabin all the work belongs to me.

Now back in the old days, every summer they'd hold what you call a "Rendezvous," where trappers and Indians alike would get together to trade their skins and furs for goods and provisions. Those were colorful and glorious affairs! Why, you'd spy old friends you hadn't seen for a year! There was plenty of time to set and chat for a spell. And for those of us who'd been up in the woods for months on end, oftentimes that was the first chance we had to eat anything 'cept old dried up hard-tack and dried meat. It was glorious!

These days though, you'll find me tradin' in my trappin's right here in Liberty Falls. I reckon folks around here consider me somethin' of an old-fashioned character in this day and age, what with telephone services, telegraph wires, and even 'lectricity becomin' commonplace in town. Seems like every time I come to town there's another mansion under construction, or a fancy downtown buildin' like that huge Clock Tower and Bell Tower — not to mention that big ole Post Office and City Hall! Why, I remember when all there was in "downtown" was a few tents and a couple 'a log cabins. Nowadays Liberty Falls looks for all the world like a miniature Denver! But like I told ya before — this is my way 'o life, up in the mountains, and I'm not of a mind to change. I'm off now...got to load up Miss Bessie for the trip up to the cabin. Hope ta see ya next month when I'm back in town! Adios!

While trappers often toiled alone, they enjoyed each others' company immensely when they could work together.

CHAPTER X

Liberty Falls: The Modern Era

An awe-filled account of some contemporary advancements in Colorado at the turn of the century...as told by the head librarian at the Liberty Falls Library and Reading Room, Constance Adams

ood afternoon! Welcome to the Liberty Falls Library and Reading Room! Make yourself at home. Here in the front of the building you'll find our reading area with overstuffed chairs and side tables, and if you walk through the doors on either side of me you'll locate our stacks. I'm proud to say we're up to 5,000 volumes, and what with our recent monetary gift from Mr. Andrew Carnegie himself, we'll soon be able to double our holdings! Now, as with any library you know, we have strict rules of silence so that our patrons may research or read in peace. But if you'll step over here to my private office, I'd

Folks in Liberty Falls really knew they had "arrived" when George Willis started delivering mail to them at home.

be delighted to tell you more about our cozy little library and a few of the other modern advancements here in Liberty Falls.

I'm Constance Adams, and I'm the head librarian here. Moved to Liberty Falls from Denver not too long ago, and land sakes, it's quite an adjustment! Through the Denver chapter of the Woman's Christian Temperance Union I learned that the Liberty Falls Ladies Temperance Society had rooms to rent in a safe, clean home — so that's where I'm staying for the time being. It's just a block away from the Library and Reading Room, and all the ladies in the Temperance Society have been very nice! Even so, living in a small town is different than bustling Denver. Just yesterday morning a baby bear loped through town in search of its mother — I saw him right out that window! And as soon as you get onto the side streets it's quite dusty because only Main Street is paved. All in all it's pleasant here though — the pace of life is slower, and people take time to chat — just like you and I are doing right now!

In Denver I had only one specialty in the library — I became an expert on European history. That was possible because The Denver Public Library has more than a dozen librarians on staff, and separate departments for folks wanting to know about Colorado history, genealogy, geography, and many more specialties. Here, no matter what you want to learn, I'll be your source of reference! At first I was worried...would I be able to meet the needs of everyone in Liberty Falls? But folks here are so downright patient and appreciative. All of our patrons — from the highly educated folks like Mrs. Clark and Mrs. DuBois to "Trapper Big Mike" — seem delighted just to have a resource in town like our Library and Reading Room! Indeed, Liberty Falls' earlier citizens like the Clarks and DuBois' remember quite vividly the days when they were living in "soddies" with absolutely no modern conveniences of any kind!

Speaking of our patrons, that Mrs. Clark really does put me into a tailspin sometimes with her requests! Just last week she was here asking for help locating some English lace patterns she remembered from her younger days "Back East." Well, in our holdings we don't have even one lace book. But luckily I was able to enlist the help of Billy Atwell over at the Pacific & Mountain Telegraph Company. He sent a telegram to Denver for me, and my old friend Nancy Bailey in the art department of the Denver Library found me just the right book, ready to lend. Mrs. Clark was so excited that she dispatched two of her daughters on a day trip to Denver via train. "Have a good time, enjoy lunch at my expense and go shopping, girls — but just remember to stop by the library and borrow my lace book," she told them. "Mention Miss Adams' name to Nancy Bailey and she'll accommodate you." I imagine maybe a couple of the Clark sons will get a similar opportunity for travel when the book is due back in Denver!

While I was visiting with Billy, I asked him to show me around his telegraph office. It really seems a marvel to me that with a few "dots and dashes" Billy can send messages just about anywhere! On my return here to the library, I couldn't resist looking up a bit of history about the telegraph — occupational hazard, you might say. What I found out was nothing short of fascinating! Did you know that Samuel Morse, inventor of "Morse code," first got the idea when he was an art student in London? At least that's what the historians speculate!

Some of the signs that Liberty Falls had entered the "modern era": Ben Cummings' fancy printing press, Billy Atwell's telegraph, and the Union Pacific's newest steam engine.

Young Samuel — born in 1791 in Charlestown, Massachusetts — enjoyed a marvelous education at Phillips Academy in Andover, and then at Yale University in New Haven, Connecticut. While in college, he became intrigued by electricity, but his main interest was art. Samuel's father — a renowned Congregational minister — was scandalized by the idea of an art career for his son, but he reluctantly agreed to send the young man to London for more training as a portraitist. Upon his arrival in London, Samuel thought fondly of his mother back home. The two were very close, and they had never been separated by such a distance before. At the age of 20, Samuel Morse wrote these words to his mother — a sentence which foreshadowed his greatest achievement: "I wish that in one instant I could tell you of my safe arrival, but we are 3,000 miles apart and must wait four long weeks to hear from each other."

Of course, Samuel knew folks had been sending signals back and forth using various types of code for hundreds of years. The word "telegraph" was coined the year after Morse was born — combining two Greek words: tele for "far," and graphein, which means "to write." Some cultures used smoke, fire and drum signals, while the Greeks themselves set up a system of alphabetic signaling using large vases in specified patterns. There was no reliable way to transmit messages outside the sight or hearing of the intended recipient, though — and that idea was what obsessed Samuel Morse.

It was not until Samuel reached the age of 41 that he was struck by the brainstorm that led to his invention. Returning from Europe on the steamship "Sully," Morse struck up a conversation with a fellow passenger who knew all about the latest experiments in electromagnetism done by Claude Chappe in France, and George Murray in England. Morse commented, "If the presence of electricity can be made visible in any part of the circuit, I see no reason why intelligence may not be transmitted by electricity." The concept developed much more quickly than the execution: my research tells me that Samuel required a good five years of work before he was ready to apply for the patent on his American Electromagnetic Telegraph.

Money was a problem. Samuel knew he would need backing to set up his telegraph wire system, but many potential funders in Europe turned him down. Then in 1843 the U.S. Congress granted him $30,000 to build a prototype stretching from Washington to Baltimore. Imagine Samuel's excitement to transmit his first message in the dot-and-dash code he had invented. Perhaps you learned this one in school: Samuel flashed the words "What hath God wrought?" and history was made!

During the years when Morse was developing the telegraph, many dismissed him as a fanatic. Some even thought he was deranged! But once his invention proved itself, Morse became an international celebrity almost overnight. Abundant wealth and fame were his as businesses including railroads, newspapers and many more found diverse uses for the telegraph. By 1850, the first underwater telegraph cable was installed from Dover, England to Calais, France, and in 1856 Western Union was founded so that telegraph wires could be strung from coast to coast here in the continental United States.

Constance Adams was so fascinated by Billy Atwell's telegraph equipment that she sat down one day to teach herself Morse Code!

You know, all this talk about code reminds me that we librarians have a helpful code of our own these days: we call it the Dewey Decimal System. And just as Samuel Morse developed a way of communicating across the country, the innovative Mr. Melvil Dewey revolutionized library science with the invention of his famous system in 1876. Dewey's concept was that decimal classification would make finding books in the library quicker — and that if every library used the same system, researchers and librarians alike would find their work considerably easier.

The Dewey system has 10 main subjects, each with a three-figure number assigned to it. The first number in the figure indicates the general subject (4 for language, 5 for science, 8 for literature as a few examples) and the other two numbers break it down further. But you can get even more specific numbers, if you need to. I'll give you an example. If you wanted to look up United States history, the Dewey number for that is 973. But let's say you want to know something about the American Revolution. It has its own number: 973.3! The more detailed the subject gets — the more minute a part it is of the main subject — the more numbers it will have after the main number. Why, in big libraries like the one in Denver you could have up to six numbers after the decimal point to lead you to a book on a pinpoint subject!

Now that the Dewey Decimal System has caught on all across the United States, the library has reached the modern age. I just can't imagine anything more satisfying than a card catalog listing every single book in the library according to its Dewey Decimal number as well as its subject, title and author. Orderly, neat, tidy and predictable. That's the way we librarians like it! And one of my greatest pleasures is to invite the Liberty Falls youngsters over here to show them how the library is set up. It seems like every class has at least a few "bookworms" — and I love it when those special children stop by each day after school to curl up in one of our overstuffed chairs and read!

You know, there seems to be something in human nature that encourages folks to seek knowledge and set up libraries. That's another thing I've studied over the years, and I always tell an abbreviated version of "library history" to the young people who visit me here. Almost as soon as humans figured out how to record the written word, they developed ways of sharing that information with others. The Chinese of the Shang Dynasty (about 1700 to 1000 years B.C.) wrote records on animal bones and tortoise shells. Egyptian libraries circa 1300 B.C. included thousands of papyrus scrolls full of valuable facts and stories. The Palace Library of Ashurbanipal was established at Nineveh, Assyria as early as the 600s B.C. But it didn't have books, land sakes, no! It housed more than 30,000 clay tablets. Can you imagine how sore my back would be at the end of a day if I had to sort and re-shelve clay tablets? Mercy!

The Greeks and Romans established libraries, but not every Tom, Dick and Harry was allowed to use them. You had to be a scholar, a noted religious figure or noble person to get access to the materials — an idea quite at odds with what we believe here in the United States of America! That religious connection held strong for many years — indeed as you probably know the monks were instrumental in copying precious books many hundreds of years ago. Keep in mind that part of the exclusivity of books was the very fact that there were so few of them: that is until after the technique of printing using mov-able type was perfected by Johannes Gutenberg in the mid-1400s. Even so, Muslims and Byzantines developed the idea of the "House of Wisdom," a university library that the public was invited to use. I love to read about the early Muslim libraries from about 800-900 A.D. Not only did they house the books, but they provided meeting places and sponsored debates! Maybe I should offer the reading room as a debate center for our Town Council?

By the 1500s there were many great libraries in Europe, mostly in university cities such as Madrid (Spain), Wittenberg and Leipzig (Germany), Graz (Austria), Wroclaw (Poland), and Vilnius (Lithuania). Latin American libraries began to thrive in that era as well, including those at the University of Santo Domingo in the Dominican Republic, and the National Autonomous University of Mexico in Mexico City. About that same time many communities and towns throughout Europe began to open. Sadly, they did not lend books, and the collections were mostly poorly arranged (no wonder we needed the Dewey system!)

Before our modern concept of the public library took hold, the American colonies had such a thing as a rental or subscription library. You could either rent books for a small, per-book fee, or become a library subscriber for so much per year. Benjamin Franklin started one of the first subscription libraries in Philadelphia way back in 1731! There were also "mercantile" or "mechanics'" libraries. These were set up by working people as a means of self-improvement, with such institutions existing in the early part of the 19th century throughout England, Canada and the United States. There were even YMCA libraries, although many of their books were religious in nature, and railroad libraries established for the use of railroad employees and passengers on long-distance trips.

In recent years, a wonderful man named Andrew Carnegie has revolutionized the way we Americans think about libraries. Mr. Carnegie was born the son of a weaver in Dunfermline, Scotland, in 1835. When he was just 13 he got a job as a bobbin boy in a cotton mill near Pittsburgh, soon after he and his family came to the United States. Highly ambitious and bright, Carnegie established his own business at the age of 30 and grew it into Pittsburgh's prosperous Carnegie Steel Company. When he was 65, Carnegie sold his business interests to J.P. Morgan for $400 million. He announced his intention to spend the rest of his life writing and strategically distributing his money.

I recently read Andrew Carnegie's 1889 book, *The Gospel of Wealth*. I was mightily impressed with his assertion that all accumulated wealth — beyond what one needs for one's family — should be considered a "community trust fund" to be administered for the good of all!

Carnegie's primary interest is in public libraries. These days he is giving away his money fast and furious for the establishment of libraries all over the English-speaking world! He started promoting public libraries in 1881 and already has given away millions for his cause. Luckily for us here in Colorado, Mr. Carnegie has taken a special interest in this state. Imagine my glee when I learned that Liberty Falls — along with many other Colorado cities large and small — would benefit from Andrew Carnegie's largess! With the money he has donated we can double the size of our holdings — and I may even be able to hire a second librarian to help extend our services! Imagine how wonderful it would be to set up story programs for youngsters, and classes for older folks who want to learn how to read or enhance their reading skills!

I first got the news that our Reading Room and Library would become a Carnegie library by way of an official letter from Mr. Carnegie himself. And that brings to mind another "modern advancement" hereabouts: we in Liberty Falls now have our own up-to-date Federal Post Office, where I went to pick up the letter in the library's post office box! And just as the telegraph and the modern library have improved the quality of life here in town, the Post Office certainly makes communication easier and faster for us all.

On top of the fancy new Post Office, we even have a mailman who brings deliveries around to some of the homes in town — a gent named George Willis. The first time I met George, he decided to test my knowledge of history: I guess he'd heard that was my specialty. "Who said this, Miss Adams? Most people think it was the first U.S. Postmaster, but that's not right. 'Neither snow, nor rain, nor heat, nor gloom of night stays these couriers from the swift completion of their appointed rounds.'" I'm embarrassed to say I didn't know right off. I imagine that like many people, I just kind of assumed this was the motto of the United States Postal Service. But when I looked it up, I learned I was off by more than 2,000 years! Herodotus the Greek historian made that comment about the King of Persia's messenger services circa 430 B.C.! And that wasn't the first postal service. Not by a far sight! Civilized folks have been able to send packages and letters to and fro in many lands since as early as 2000 B.C.!

But getting back to Liberty Falls, if you've been around these parts for awhile perhaps you remember the Pony Express. In its day, folks believed that was the swiftest transportation of mail they'd ever see! In certain eras the stagecoach transmitted mail, and then once we had railroads here in Colorado, they took over much of the mail carriage. When I was a girl, the Post Office was part of the General Store in most towns. I remember as a child, one of my schoolmates was the General Store owner's daughter. Little Amy had a job each day after school. She'd go down to the train station with a bag of outgoing mail, and wait on the platform for the Westbound 3:54 p.m. train to arrive. In a split second, she'd hand up the outgoing mail and receive the incoming. Then she'd skip back to her father's store so he could sort the mail for the townsfolk. Along about 5 p.m., people would start filtering in to see if they had any letters or packages. Amy's father loved having the Post Office in his store, because few people could resist making a purchase or two after they checked their mail cubbyhole! Nowadays the Post Office is a much more formal operation, though. We have official postal employees selected and trained by the U.S. Government for their jobs, as George Willis so proudly informs us.

Oh, I see "Trapper Big Mike" coming up the front steps for his monthly visit. I'll let you have a look around while I'm helping him find the books he wants to borrow. What an inspiration he is to me: never went past fourth grade, but each month he fills his knapsack with a dozen or so books on many topics — and then when he comes back to town to trade in his furs and skins, he stops by to turn in the books and get more. Mike reads every evening by the light of the fire in his cabin — so widely and on so many topics that I'd call him Liberty Falls' own "Renaissance man." I'll say good-bye to you now so I can greet him. Happy reading!